Serpents

and Other Spiritual Beings

September 2022

Published by Kegedonce Press
11 Park Road, Neyaashiinigmiing, ON N0H 2T0
Administration Office/Book Orders: P.O. Box 517, Owen Sound, ON N4K 5R1
www.kegedonce.com

Printed in Canada by Gilmore Printing
Cover artwork and illustrations: Bomgiizhik Isaac Murdoch
Translation: Patricia BigGeorge
Author's photo: Alex Usquiano
Design: Chantal Lalonde Design

Stories transcribed from Bomgiizhik Isaac Murdoch's oral storytelling.

Library and Archives Canada Cataloguing in Publication

Title: Serpents and other spiritual beings / author and illustrator,
    Bomgiizhik Isaac Murdoch ; translator, Patricia BigGeorge.
Names: Bomgiizhik, 1975- author, illustrator.
Description: Series statement: Ojibwe history series ; vol. 2 |
    In Anishinaabemowin translation and in original English.
Identifiers: Canadiana 20220391920 | ISBN 9781928120353 (softcover)
Subjects: CSH: First Nations—Canada—Folklore. | LCGFT: Folk tales.
Classification: LCC E99.C6 B66 2022 | DDC 398.2089/97333—dc23

For Customer Service/Orders
Tel 1–800–591–6250 Fax 1–800–591–6251
100 Armstrong Ave. Georgetown, ON L7G 5S4
Email: orders@litdistco.ca or visit www.kegedonce.com

We acknowledge the support of the Canada Council for the Arts which last year
invested $20.1 million in writing and publishing throughout Canada.

The Canada Council Le Conseil des Arts
  for the Arts   du Canada
  since 1957   depuis 1957

We would like to acknowledge funding support from the Ontario Arts Council,
an agency of the Government of Ontario.

ONTARIO ARTS COUNCIL
CONSEIL DES ARTS DE L'ONTARIO
50 YEARS OF ONTARIO GOVERNMENT SUPPORT OF THE ARTS
50 ANS DE SOUTIEN DU GOUVERNEMENT DE L'ONTARIO AUX ARTS

I would like to dedicate this book
to my Beautiful Daughter Elaine
and my Grandchildren.

CONTENTS

GAA'MOOKINIGAADEG

Misi-ginebek Aadizookaanan

Gitashimind misi ginebekoog jiitaw ayaad dazhimindaa igi binesaweg, dibishkoo gi'zagininjiiniwe. Gegaa dibhiskoo gawiin dashimind mashkode bizhiki gawisowegaad gawiin michhi'izhijigma mashkode bizhiki. Iniw andawen dibaajimowan igiwe misi-ginebedkoog ozaam niminjimendan giji-aa'aag gimamagwe'inidiwad miidash gaa manidooke iwe jiigi-ziibi gaye bebakaan zaaga'inganing. Mii'inowaan zenibaan gaye mitigoonsag.

Ezhi ozhitoonwad ino bagijiganan igiwe misi-ginebekoog binjitaziibiing adish gaye binjitazaagan'iganian. Ikidog ayaawan zhiigewenan izhijigadagan babaa waawaagizinoon ima aki anaamakamig, iwe dish zhiigewenan izhijigadagan ayaawad misi-ginebekoog, geya niiibi aya'aag babaa-ayaad. Aapii ino zhiibaayaabikaa' mooshkamogan biinji zaaga'iganan, mii'ima aapii giji aa'aag izhi bagijige'ad. Ninoondaw giinawind inowaan aatzokaninan i'i zhiigewenan izhaa anaamaki, dibi-go iwe izhiigewenan mooshkamo' waawendaagwa ayaag igiwe giwiji aa'aag. Mi'ima gii'igoshimoong wigikendamaawinan ozaam gagikendamin iwedi gegoo ayaag anaamaki, gegoo gichi-nitaagiwi'an.

INTRODUCTION

Serpent Stories

You can't really talk about Serpents without talking about Thunderbirds, they kind of go hand-in-hand. It's almost like you can't really talk about a buffalo hunter without talking about a buffalo. The reason why I wanted to talk about serpents is because I remember years ago the Elders would gather and they would have ceremonies at the river and the different lakes. Which was ribbons and sticks.

They'd make these offerings to the Serpents inside the rivers and the lakes. They say that there's a tunnel system that zigzags across the land underneath the ground, and in this tunnel system is where the Serpents and the underwater beings travel. Where these tunnels come up into the lakes, that's where our people would make those offerings. Most of us have heard about the stories of these tunnels that go underneath, wherever that tunnel came up was a very sacred place for our people. We would fast there for knowledge because we know that there's something down below, something very powerful.

Misi-ginebek apane gii-andema gimiigaadiing, gibakademigad, aakosiwinan. Gii-andema iko ji'ayaad mino-wyaawinan, jii-ganawendaagosi'ad ga-onji-andomin.

Aapi'iwi NODAPL (Gawiin Bwannakiing Bi-naazikaw Onagizhiyaabin) gaye apii gakina onagizhiyaabinan/aajionagizhiyaabinan aanjigoziwin, apane ikidoog iwe "Nizaa makade-ginebek". Gii'anishinaabeyan, nitaawigiigo ji debwetaman bakaan. Akina inaadiziwinan odibendanawan inendamowinan gaye debwetamowinan, mi'iwa bezhing naabinigan. Awii sa anishinaabeg gaa onji'an akiins, ndebwetamin iwe misi-ginebek giji zoongizid aa'aa. Gi aa'aawa'ing, gaanizhogadtewin, gawiin nika gigashkitoonziin jinizit nisaa gegoo igo.

Iwe manitooke ga'iiyad anaamaki aapi gichi-inendaagwad jidibishkoowendaagwad iwi aki. Apii animiki-bensiwag gaye misi-ginebekoog miigaadiwad, aanike-amwaade idish, gigikendam, gichi-mas'yad hkiki ondaasin agaamaya'ii akinang. Mi'ooma Bimaadiziwin onjiimagag. Naasaab izhiwebizi mashkode-bizhiki giiyosewinini michi-wiijigaabawitaadiwin iwi mashkode-bizhiki, mamawimwiinawaa aanike-odegan, wiinawaa naagadawendamowinan. Midish bekish mashkode-bizhiki giiyosewinini onizaan mashkode-bizhiki, aangoodinong mashkode-bizhiki oganizhan iw anishinaaban. Wii'iw naasaab bezhigwanong, wii'iw naasaab wiijigaabawitaadiwin'.

The Serpent was often called upon during times of war, famine, disease. It was called upon so that we could have good health and be protected. During the NODAPL (No Dakota Access Pipe Line) and during this whole pipeline/anti-pipeline movement, there's often a lot of talk about "kill the black snake." As an Anishinaabeg, I was raised to believe differently. Every culture has its own way of thinking and believing, it's all a piece of the puzzle. For the Anishinaabeg in my region, we believe that the Serpent is a very powerful being. As humans, as two-legged people, we'd never be able to kill something like that.

The power that's down there is very critical for the balance of this Earth. When the Thunderbirds and the Serpents fight, when they feed off each other, you know, great medicine gets cast across the land. We get our life from that. The same way that a buffalo hunter has a special relationship with a buffalo, together their hearts are connected, their minds. Yet at the same time the buffalo hunter will kill the buffalo, sometimes the buffalo will kill the Indian. It's the same sort of thing, it's the same sort of relationship.

Zhigwa'apii ozhitowaang bagiiga'nan wiinawaa misi-
ginebekook jita aabinoojiiyag jii-ganawendaagosi'ad
niibikang, mi'igo gakina inoodewizinan aakinang
jibimaadiziwad, nanaandoowinan bagosendanan,
gawiinawa chi-ganawenimindwa. Azhigane-ayi'ii niinawiin
giishkiganan, niinawin agwiinan, gidagobiindewan
onowan bagijiganan wiidgashkibijigan jii-gikendamowad
wiinawaa'igo omiinigoziniwaan gibiina'igaatemaweg.
Shke idish, gimoozhaginigemin iwe begwa'iganan giishkiganiwan
wiinawa ninijaansinaaneg, gakina anishinaabeweg gaye
oodemag, mii'imaa gachigataagin iniwaan bagijiganan
a'iing gashkibijigan, a'ii agibiindaakoojige gaye. Aapiji
giji apiitendaagwad, mii iwi azhigane-ayi'ii bigwajaya'ii
inaakonaganaan. Aaniish mii'iwi ogimaakandimang noopiming
iozhitoon gibagijigenan, mii' iwa gaa izhi bimaadiziwin a'a aki
gaa manidookag.

Aapiji nimamgadaadem iwi gii ikidoowad "iwa nzaagi'aki, niin
iwe?". Apii iko ningiiwose'ang, gikendamin igiwe manidoowag,
igi memegwesiwak, ji ginebek, gaye animikiiwag bimaadiziwad
iwedi ingoji. Igi bakaan manidoowad gaa bimaadiziwad ingoji,
odibendanayad igo ga'ozhige'ad. Gikendamin iwe niinetawin
bigwajaya'ii gaa izhigewad. Mii'dish, nimamgadaadem jii
inandaman niinata iwi aki, gii ayaaad aa'aa gawiin idish.

Bigwajaya'ii o'o ogimaakandawaanan onjiimagadoon
gii bagijigenan, gii miigiwemin bagijigenan apane. Onh,
memegwesiwak gii izhitaawag iwedi, igi misi-ginebegook gii
izhitaawag, binesiwag daa ayaanawan animikiiwazison ingoji.
Mozhag igo miigiwem, miigiwem, miigiwem o'o aki, miigiwem
gaye igo aamanidoowag ayaad ingoji. Onizhishi bimaadiziwin.
Mii' iwe aanishaa bi izhaga'ashkag iwe gaakikinige gegoo gii
odaapinimiing, mi'inowan bagijigenan.

It was this time of year, spring, when we made our offerings to those Serpents so that our children could be safe in the waters, so that our families were out living their lives on the land, when we made those petitions, they would be looked after. Parts of our clothes, our garments, would be offered with that bundle so that they would know that a present was offered on their behalf. So, we would take little pieces of our clothes from our children, our babies and all our people and family, and that would be put into that bundle with offerings of tobacco. That was very, very important, that's part of our natural laws. How we govern ourselves in the forest is by making those offerings, so that we can live in a land of spirits.

It's very odd to me when we say, "This is my traditional territory, this is mine!" When we used to trap, we knew that the spirits, the Memegwesiwak, the Chi-ginebig, and the Thunderers lived out there. The different spirits that lived out there, they all had their own homes. We knew that we were only a part of their home. So, it's very odd for me to think that this land is only mine, as a human being it's not.

Part of the governance is through our offerings; we give offerings all the time. Oh, the Memegwesiwak lived there, the Serpents lived here, Thunderbirds have a nest up there. All the time we're giving, giving, giving to the land, giving to the spirits that are out there. It's a beautiful life. It's how we're able to restore the balance of what we take, is through our offerings.

Aanish, ayaa onjinewinan gishpin megwaa gii izhijige'sii. Gishpin gagwe wendizin magizha gaye zasagizewin gaa wii bagijigean igi aa'aag, gooding ayaa enaginde diba'igem. Iwi akii, enji bimaadizid iniwi gizhewaasdziwimagak gakina gegoo. Ino inaakonigewinan gemaa bigwajaya'ii inaakonogenan ima aki daa ayaan gizhewaadizimagak. Shke idash, giishpin odaapinige'ing, odaapinige'ing, odaapinige'ing aa'i gaye gawiin gegoo miigiwesiim…. Mi'idish aaniin iw? Maagizhw giiwaabidemin aanid maazhise.

Wiinawa ikidoyad misi-ginebek niimida-ginwaabigozid, agaasinike a'ii gaye agaasigigaade, saagiwine gaye eshkanan oshtigwaaning. Iwi misi-ginebek okanan miskwaabik inowaan, ikidowed. Inoodewiziwiniyeg wiinawa ezhi ayabitaad.

Noongom igo ganoona niwiji-maamakaadendaagozi iti wenji Deshkan Ziibiing ishkonigan. Nii-maamakaadendan o'oo misi-ginebek aadizookan ozaam iizan, ogiwaabamaan l'no misi-ginebig. Mi'idish igo shamaag nibaajiikaweg dibishkoo waabanomin, niin dish "Jiitaw dibaajimo'izhin! Jiitaw-wiindamow wegonen izhisegm, "gakina gegoo dibaajimon." Gakina gegoo dibaajimo gi-waabanjigaad, mi'idish maaji waabi'odengwaan gidibaajimood ozaam ji-zegizi. Izhise igo iwi bigwajaya'ii ozaamakama iwe odanemiing ayaag gishpin gii waabimind misi-ginebek. Jitaa igo jii ayaag iwe dibishkookaw gotaajiwin gaye iwe dibishkookaw "Gaa naa" na'aa?

Iniwan aadizookanan, ndibaajimowan aaniish bemaadizi'ad wenji izhise'ad misi-ginebekogizhiiwi'ad goding inakamigad. Mii' gegoo iwe apane nwiikoshkaagon, gii abinojii'yan gaye nitaagiwi, iwe gwekaa-onzhio' gemaa gaye bimaadiziwad onzhio'daa awesiineg. Iwe misi-ginebek giji mashkawaa aa'aa. Ikidoogd iwe niimida-ginwaabigozid, ayaad onikan, okaadan gaye eshkanan. Apiji giji mashkawayaa zasaagodizi gaye wii'gitamowa' gabemaadiziwad goding eta.

Of course, there are consequences when you don't do that. If you're trying to be cheap or stingy and not giving your offerings to these things, sometimes there is a price to pay. This land, it lives on the generosity of everything. The rules or the natural laws that the land has is generosity. So, if we keep taking, taking, taking and we don't give anything back... well then guess what? We can probably expect some hard times.

They say that the Serpent is forty feet long, it's got little arms and legs, it's got horns sticking out of its head. The bones of the Serpent are made of copper, they say that. They live in families.

Just today I spoke to an amazing friend of mine in Chippewa of The Thames First Nation. I was curious about a Serpent story because apparently, he's seen a Serpent. I'm like right on him like white on rice, I'm like "you GOTTA tell me! You gotta tell me what happened, tell me everything!" He told me about what he had seen, and his face went pale when he talked about it because he was very scared. It's a natural reaction that we're supposed to have if we see a Serpent. There should be a level of fear and a level of "OMG" right?

The stories I want to tell involve about how people were turned into Serpents under certain circumstances. This is something that has always fascinated me, as a child and growing up, was shape shifting or people that got turned into animals. The Serpent is a very powerful being. They say that it's over forty feet long, it's got arms, legs and horns. It's very powerful, magical and will eat humans if it must.

Misi-ginebek Neyaashing

Mewinzha ikidowad, iwi oshkininis, An-ishinaabes o'o, ogii'izhi nawaad ima waawen-daag igoshimowa'yan, jimakadekewin, i'iwidi Shkoodeyiing minis ezhinikaade. Mi'iwidi gaa-izhi'ined j-imakadekewin a'ii ji-naagwe'idizowin ogodinaan wiineta bawaajigan gaye miinigoo-wiziwin

Apii megwa gii'igoshimod, gegoo gi'izhise. Igiwi anishinaabeg gaa-izhinawad gi wiinda-maagowiziweg "Migo iwate onji-iganiganawaa. Mi'iwi oshkininis otayaan giji-minigozi mani-tooke gaye wiinigo dibi-giiwe. Gawiin gaa naaz-ko'ise"

Mi'iwi oshkininis, ashi niizh-bibone, mi'iwate minising gii'nagana. Shkoodeyiing wiineta. Giwiindamaa'aag gawiin azhegiiwesiim gawiin gaa naazko'ise. Misa, iwate namadabi endaso-giizhik. Gawiin miijim, gawiin nibi, gaawiin gegoo. Wiin gii-gikinaamowa ji- anami'aa iwi win jii'igoshimowin, midash ga-izhichiged.

Gegapii , giji giishkaabaagwe gaye bebengwani-yeg, bakaakadwaa'odengwaan. Wegonen igo gagwaizhijige wii'maajaa iwi minis. Gi'ikido'oog gibazigwiid gimaajaa gagi'abid, wenji ogikendaan gegoo wimaazhise.

CHAPTER ONE

Serpent's Point

They say that years ago there was a young boy, little Anishinaabe, they went to go put him on a sacred fast, a vision quest, at a place called Shkoodeyiing, the Place of Fire is what that island is called. They put him out to fast there so that he could get his vision and get his power.

During his fast, something happened. The people that were going to put him out were told spiritually by something, "You have to leave him there. That boy has great power, and he can make his way back. Don't go get him."

So that little boy, he's only like twelve years old, was left on that island, Shkoodeyiing, by himself! They were told not to go back and get him. So, he sat there day after day after day. No food, no water, nothing. He was just instructed to pray for his vision so that's what he did.

Finally, he got so thirsty and dehydrated, his face just sucked right in! He was ready to do whatever he could to get off the island. They say that he got up and left his spot, because he knew something was wrong.

Gibimose agamiing onawaabidan gitakmaigaang, ginawaabi igo maamakaadedam wegonen dash anishinaabeg gaa maajaawaad. Mi'iwidi geba-dibik abid, jiigibiiskaa iwidi.

izhaa iwedi (gawiin niin iwi oshkininis), gii zhaa iwidi ozaam wiikoshkaagon iwi dibaajimowin

Iwi oshkininis jigibiing gi'iizhaa jiigibiing, mii'imaa ginibaa jigibiing. Ingo-dibik bawaajige. Gawiin eta bawaajigan idash gaye onwaachigewin waagonen gaa izhiwebizeg, ogiwaabandan,wii'ani-akiiwang awaajigewin.

Obawaajigewin, miitaawangang inaabi, endash zaagaakosin makade ozowns imaa mii-taawangang, mamaajise, migo gii'aabe waaban-dang. Gezika iwaa ozowens michaase, idash mii-taawang gaye mamaajise miinawaa igo mamajise. Migo gi'aabe giinowaabandang iwaa obwaajigeniing.

Gezika mookii makade ginebekoons, idash iwi ginebek wendamawan: "Goshkozi'in beedaa-bang, miitaawangang ige inaab. Agibi-indaakoojige imaa

Gaa ezhi biindaakoojigeyan, gabi'naazikowa. Igi waabidan miitaawang daa maaji ditibise, mi'idash gaa waabimin iwedi." I'i oshkininis mii' bijiinag goshkozid idash mooga'ang biijinag, giji'amigad apii, apiji mashkawayaa api ezhi giizhig.

Gibi mooga'ng mii' zhemaag maaji waabidang o'o miitawaang. Gibiindaakoonige, odaa ase-maman, migo nasab gikinoo'amaa o'bwaajigan. Moozhag igo ima namadabi migo gino waabidang iwi mitaawang. Gawiin gegoo izhise-noon. Magizhaa ditibise gi'inendaam. Ezhi basangwaabid maaji gagnoonaad iwi anamaka-miing. Gikido "Nii'ayaa ima! Niin awe oshkininis gaganoozh dibikong Nii'ayaa ima! Mii'ima geizhi nibowin; Ninenandan wiji'ishiin. Daga bizhaan ayaa'an.

He walked to the shoreline looking at the mainland, just staring at it wondering why his people left. So, he spent the night there, there's a little beach there. I have been there (no I wasn't the little boy), I went there because I was fascinated by the story.

The little boy goes to the beach, he sleeps on the beach. That night he had a dream. Not only a dream but he had a prophecy of what was going to happen, onwaachigewin, he's seen the future in his dream.

In his dream he looked into the sand, and he saw a little black tail sticking out of the sand, it was moving around, and he kept staring at it. All of a sudden that little tail started to get bigger, and the sand started to move around and around. He just kept staring at it in his dream.

All of a sudden a little black snake emerged, and that snake told him: "When you wake up in the morning, I want you to come look in the sand. Put some tobacco there."

"Where you put the tobacco, I'll come for it. You will see the sand start turning around, and I'll see you there." The boy just woke up and of course the sun was just coming up, that's a very powerful time of the day.

The sun was just coming up and right away he started to look in that sand. He put asemaa there, his tobacco, just like he was instructed in the dream. He sat there for a long time and stared at that sand. Nothing happened. It didn't start to twirl around like he thought. So, he closed his eyes and he spoke to that ground underneath. He said "I'm here! I'm the little boy you spoke to last night. I'm here! I'm going to die here; I need your help. Please come to me!"

Gezika, iwi mitaawang maaji gizhebaatite nana'akaaj. Owaabidan iwi ozowens mookiseg gaa ezhiise igo obawaajigan. Gawiin ji deb-weyendang! Iwe maajii-ditibise giyaabi igo ditibise mino waa ditibise. Geg aapii, makade ginebekonz, makade mnidooawaash, mookiid imaa mitaawangang

Iwi makade ginebekoonz owaabimigoon mi'idash ji-widamowad: "Ingii-noondoon Gibi-indaakoonigen, Omaa daa ayaa, Nadawenimin jibisangwaabi'in ,mii' ga bagosenjige igiwe wiiji aa'aag… ozaam gii-giji-zanagak bi'ayamagad. Izhi-boaosenjige'an, giji-bagosenjige'an, gaa nmin-did. Awashime giyaai bagosenjige'an migo noowaaj gaa ini mindid.

Misa, gizhichigad iwi oshkininis. Gimaaji ba-gosenjiged igo bagosenjiged, maaji bagosen-jigedamaw wiiji aa'aag, mii'iwe gii-giji-zanagak gaa bi ayamagad. Iwi misi-ginebek ginwaabiigizid, misa giji min-dido! Gawiin ogikendaziin owaananidbiigizid ozaam gibazengwaabi. Dash inaabid ayaa ima giji misi-ginebek shigishin iwe jiigibiig, niim-idana ginwaabigizi, giji eshakanan!

Ini eshakanan mashkwaa'igan, inaadiziwin gikendamowin. Iwe misi-ginebek oginawaabima ino gwiizensan izhi ikido, "Giji-inenimin. Nigii-wewinan. Gwashkonin ima nipickwan, minjimi-inan nieshkanan! Ga aashoogwinin ide Ne-yaashiing, neyaashi."

Iwi oshkininis gwaashkwaini ima misi-ginebek opikwanang, minjimaakwid ino eshkanan, mii'iwe misi-ginebek aashawa'inad iwedi Ne-yaashiing. Ga izhi bagidinend o'o oshinnins ezhi ikido, "Niin Ginebig, Niin iwi ginebek. Niin genawendaan inowaan nibi'. Gii miizhiwin iko gaa daa asema gaa minomanji'o. Apane gikendan imaa a'yaan, apane gikendan gibi-indaakoojige'yan."

Suddenly, that sand started to move around very slowly. He could see that little tail come out just like in his dream. He couldn't believe it! That thing just started to go around and around and around. Finally, a little black snake, a little black mnidooawaash, came out of the sand.

That little black snake looked at him and told him: "I heard you. You put your tobacco down, I'm here. I want you to close your eyes and I want you to pray for your people… because hard times are coming. As you pray, the harder you pray, the more that I'll grow. The more that you pray for your people the bigger I'll get!"

So that's what the boy did. He started to pray, and pray, and pray for his people, for the hard times that were going to come. That Serpent started to grow, it got real big! He didn't even know how big it was because his eyes were closed, but when he opened his eyes there was a great big serpent laying on the beach, forty feet long, great big horns!

Those horns are very powerful, they represent knowledge. That serpent looked at that boy and said, "I'm very proud of you. I will take you back home. Jump onto my back, hold onto my horns! I'll take you across to Neyaashiing, the point."

The little boy jumped onto the Serpent's back, held onto those horns, and the Serpent took him across to Neyaashiing. It dropped the boy off and said, "I'm Ginebig, I'm the snake. I am the guardian of these waters. When you gave me your tobacco it made me feel good. Always know that I'm here, always know that I'm watching."

Ozaam iwe oshinnis gaa mijimaadk onno eshkana
gi'aashawa'oonid iwe nibi, gikenda-mowin aashawa'aa
iwe eshkanan gaye biiinjiseg owiiyaw. Iwa gikendamowin
gaa onjiseg o'o misi-ginebek biijinseni owa mii' maajii
giji mashkwaasuu nashkikinini ozaam giminjiminang ino
eshkanan.

Oskinnins ani izhaa ininaabikoog abid neyaashi-iwan iwedi
mii' oodaapinang anind onaman, iwe miskwa zhizhoobii'igan
inaabadag mzainibii'igdag ozhibii'igen inowaan bawaajiganan
imaa ininaabikoog. Mii' daabiip-idood iwe miskwa
zhizhoobii'igan mii' zhi-zhoobii'iged o'o misi-ginebeg ima.
Chimaamiikwenodaage babaamizi endanakami-gak mii'igiwe
niizho'okaade'ad gaye giji misi-ginabek. Iwi oshkinnins gi
ombigid ani giji'mashkwase niigaanizi ozaam gimin-jiminang
inowaan eshkanan.

Noongom izhi-wiinde iwi: Ginebig Neyaashiing, Misi-ginebek
neyaashi. Maagizha gaye Gichi-GinebeigNayaashiing, gijii
ginebek neyaashi. Baamaa daso-biboon, wiji aa'aa gaiyaabi
izhaad giji waawendaagaa ayaag onda bagijigeng iwedi,
oda asemamiya'. Ozaam apii misi ginebig bagidinaadd ino
gwiizensan izhinaad o'no osh-kinninsan mii azhaad anaami
izhiigewenan mi-inawa, migo ima neyaashi. Mi'sa bigwajaya'ii
wiji aa'aag ezhinaawad iwedi.

Apii igi Naadoweg, iwi neshenim gaa bii'izhaawad, iwedi
izhaad iwedi gaye izhi big-agwedwewinan ji ganawejigaazo'ad
ezhi odoo-demi'ad. Daso-biboonagad, aa'aag azhaad iwedi,
igi ozhitoonewad bagijigenan. Zenibaang mito-goonsag, iwi
zenibaanh gaye mitigoonsag.

Because that boy was holding onto those horns when he was going across that water, the knowledge came through those horns and into his own body. That knowledge from that serpent went inside of him and he became a very, very powerful medicine man because he held onto those horns.

The little boy went to the rock that was there at the point and he grabbed some onaman, that red paint that's used to mark our visions on the rocks. He grabbed that red paint and painted that Serpent on there. To commemorate the transaction that took place between the two-legged and the Great Serpent. That boy grew up to become a very powerful leader because he held onto those horns.

Now they call that place: Ginebig Neyaashiing, Serpent's Point. Or Gichi-Ginebig Neyaashiing, the Big Snake Point. Years later, our people were still going to that very sacred place to make their offerings there, their tobacco. Because when the Serpent dropped that boy off it went under the tunnel again, right there at that point. So naturally our people would go there.

When the Naadoweg, the enemies would come, they would go there and make their petitions so that they could protect their families. For years and years, our people went there, they made their offerings. Zenibaanh mitigoonsag, the ribbons and the sticks.

Mii' gegoo izhiseg. eibone aapii ningo-dosagoons shaa zhaangashwaak ashi niizh, gaa gi'akamigag iwi Gichi-Ginebig Neyaashiing. Iwi wemitigoozhi-anami'ewigamig anookiiwad ino mazinibaganjigan, ino gijiwaawendaagwad mazinibaganjigan, ini mazinibii'iganan iwi ima ininabikoog... anookiiwad nishiwanaaji'inda.

Izhawad iwedi endazhi'kamegag iwedi enda-zhiwad mamzinibee'iganan ayaagan, izhawad iwedi ogii-izhiwidoona'aad baasaabikiziganan. Hay' hay' BAASAABIKIZIGANAN! Gibaashkizo-doonayan iwe, misa aa'aag gawiin giyaabi manidookewad iwedi, misa gawiin giyaabi aa'aag maskawiziiwin onjise'noon igiwe mash-kwaa anaamaki aa'aag Ozaam igiwe nandawen-damowinan chi-gwannajigewad ji nisendwa zhigwa jigimoodiwad iwi aki.

Shke akiwenzii a'ayaa ima danakiiwin, ima ni-danakiiwan. Ezhinikaazo Giwegoom, gii'izhaa iwedi oshkwaa baasaabikisiga'a iwe ogi ayaan bagone'igans, gaa begone'iged iwa misi-ginebek minowaa ima ininabikoog. Bagosenjiged wiji aa'aag. Mamikwendam iwe dibaajimowin o'o oshkininins izhaabizid gaye gibagijige iwedi endazhi'wag, giyaabi aate iwedi noongom.

Misawaa iwi anami'aawin gigagwe ba-naajitoonawa gii wiijigaabawitaadowing big-wajaya'ii aki gaye Jiibay aki, wijii'ayaag zoonga-dized gaye ezhi basabaagadeg. Niminjimenda-min aadiskookaan; niminjimendamin wegonen ezhiseg omaa akiing. Gaawiikaa ji'odaapin ni-mowaad gii'ode'an, ginawind biinjaya'ii ama-gad. Ginidibaajimotoon iwaa.

But then something happened. The year was 1952, it happened at Gichi-Ginebig Neyaashiing. The Catholic Church ordered those pictographs, those sacred mazinibaganjigan, those paintings that were on those rocks... they ordered them to be destroyed.

They went to that site where those pictures were, they went there with dynamite. Frickin DYNAMITE! They blew them up so that our people would not worship there, so that our people wouldn't get the strength from those powerful underground beings. Because they wanted them to be weak so that they could kill them and steal their land.

But there was an old man in the village, in my village. His name was Giwegoom, he went there after they blew it up with a little chisel, and he chiseled that Serpent back into that rock. He prayed for his people. He remembered the story about what that boy went through and made his offerings there at that place, and it's still there today.

Even though the Church tried to destroy our relationship with the natural world and the spirit world, our people are strong and they're very resilient. We remember the stories; we remember what happened on our lands. They will never be able to take that away from our hearts, it's inside of us. I wanted to share that with you.

Ikidog igiwe misi-ginebekoog waawan eyaagan anaamkamig, mii' ima ginebigoonsag ayaad, oowaawano'. Ikidog iwe Zhaaganaash, ikidog i'i zhaaganaash ogandawendanaan ono waawano ozaam wiinowa ji ayaad gaa mashkawi'aa wiinetawa.

Giishbin niisay'iinh izhaad odappinaamowad iwe waawano gaa mashkawi'aa oshpishkaama-gad, mish'igo ozaam giinawind daa zoongi'yaa mii' daa banaajise o'o aki. Aazha giiwaabidamin iwi noongom. Ndebwetan o'o gaabagijigeng gaye mino'izhiwebiziwinan igiwe jiibayag gaa ayaad ima aki gaye wiinowa, gaa zhaabowii'min wegodogwen'igo bagami ayaag.

They say that the Serpents' eggs are underneath the ground, that's where their babies are, their eggs. They say that the zhaaganaash, they said the white man is going to want those eggs so that they can have that power for themselves.

If they go down and get those eggs and bring that power up, it's going to be too strong for us and it can destroy the Earth. We're seeing that today. I believe that it's through our offerings and through our good manners and our generosity with the spirits of this land and each other, that we can survive whatever comes.

BAKEBII'IGAN NIIZH

Megwaa awiyag ani-izhise misi-ginebekoog naadamaage

Bezhiig iwa dibaajimowanan nidazhindan iwi dibaajimowan ninoondaman niishtanashi-naana baboon gaa noondam iwi getaadiziwid onjii Baawitigong. Wiinawaa dibaajimog gijiinaapinewin bagami-ayaa iwedi danakiiwin.

Apii iwi naabikwaanan dagoshinoog igi adaaweininiwag, wanaii'igeininiwas, waye-zhingewininiwag, agaamakiingzhaaganaash, igi dagoshinoowad o'o naabikwanan. Aakoziwinbiidoonwad aazhookoodinidwa anishinaabeg. Nimikwendan noondaman gidibaajimowad getaadiziwad gaa ji'izhaad iwe naabikwaanan ozaam aakoziwi, ogikendanawan iiwe.

Gaa anishinaabekaa, iwedi Agawa, gaa on-ji'igonawan iwi gijii-inaapinewin. Nimaami-donenindam, iwi izhi'wiinzoog Shingebis doo-dam (maagisha mayaganishinaabe) dibishkoo amikoshib. Mii' igiwe Anishinaabek. Gijii-inaapinewin izhaamigad gaa odanakiiwad, gaki-na maaji-aakozi.

Mii', bezhiig inini giji-aakozi. Gii maaji gizhizo, gii maaji abwezo, gii maaji dakaji, mii' bwaana'ad jigiizhoozid. Megwa iwi bezhiig gizhizozid ogi'ayaan izhinamowin.

CHAPTER TWO

When People Turn into Serpents to Help Them

One of the stories I want to talk about is a story I heard about twenty-five years ago from an Elder in Sault Ste. Marie. They talked about how the plague came into the village.

When the ships came in with the traders, the trappers, the politicians, the British, the zhaaganaash, they would come in with their ships. The sicknesses that they had would get to the native people. I remember hearing stories from Elders stating that people weren't allowed to go to the ships because they were going to get sick, so our people knew that.

There was a band of Indians, down by Agawa, they got hit hard by this plague. From what I remember, they were called the Shingebis clan (or tribe), like a wood duck. They were Anishinaabek. The plague moved into their village, everybody started to get sick.

Well, this one man got really sick. He started to have fevers, he started to sweat, he started to get really chilly, they couldn't keep him warm. It was during one of those fevers that he had a vision.

Iwi izhinamowin a'a ikwe biwaabamigoon ezhi wiindamawa, "Aaniish gi'izhichiige iwi gakina gaa giijiikwanaye gaye gibakobii nibikang mii'ima gidashishinin. Bimaagoshinin, nibi gaki-na awesiinyenseg gaa bi-naazikagoog gaye baa-bajiishkamigog jiigiin.

Manoo igi gaa amogo. Maaji bajiishkamigog jiigiin gaye amogowin, gi'wiiyaw daa aanjise, gii aanjise biinji ginebek. Bezhigwa iwe izhiseg, gaa wiindima gakina awii'aa gaa wiizhaama. Jimaajinizhikaa iwi aakoziwin, jitaa igo gaa zaaminigo. Giishpin zaaminigowin, jita igo zhemaag dabakobii'oog imaa nibikaa, migo maajigiige'ad.

Mii gigoshkozi iwi giji-gizhizowi igo we-kwaanaamo, gibagak-bawaajige dibishgoo giizhi-gad. Giijikonaye'. Wiindamaw ono mindimooyenh, "Ndinendam maadaadiziwan ima; jitaa jizhichige'an iwa gegoo Minokawetaman we bawaajigen." Mii' gaa izhi-jiige, izhaa agamiing bitaagwazhe mii mitaakwa-zheshin iwedi.

Gimaaji-agonjin jiigibiig. Gezike giigoozensag bii-izhaa, omiskosii'ansag bii-izhaa, zagas-kwayensag bii-izhaa, gakina igiwe awesiiny-ensag bii-izhaa, maaji bajiishkami'ad ini, migo nasab iwe ikwe gaa wiindamagwad bwaajigan.

The vision was this lady came to him and told him, "What you have to do is you have to take all your clothes off and you have to go into the water and lie there. When you're lying there, all the little animals in the water will come to you and they'll start pecking at you."

"Let them eat you. As they start pecking at you and eating you, your body will change, you'll change into a snake. Once that happens, tell everybody to come. To get rid of that sickness, they have to touch you. If they touch you, they have to go right into the water, then they'll be healed."

He woke up from his incredible fever with a gasp, the dream was as clear as day. He took off his clothes. He told his old lady, "I think I'm going on a journey here; I need to go do this thing according to this dream." He did, he went to the lake naked and he laid there.

He started floating in the shoreline. All of a sudden little minnows came, little water bugs came, little bloodsuckers came, all these little animals came, and they started pecking at him, just like what that lady told him in his dream.

Gaget igo, mikawaabandan okaadan ani makadegan, gaa maaji onaga'ayansan ima. Maaji bazagosegan o'o okaadan, zhizhoobii'onoon okaadan, jizinigwishinoon okaadan. Mii' gosha, okaadan maaji izhinaagog onzow, dibishkoo ginebek ozhigwan. Wiiba Igo anaami-owiiyaw giginebekiwi, mii' maaji bagizo ima nibi.

Wiindamawa owiwian, "Maajaan naaziko gakina awii'aa, wiindamaw ima jibi'izhaad. Giishpin wibimaadiziwad, jitaa igo gizaaminigoo!" Geget, gaa zhijiget, gi'izhaa iwedi gaye wiindamaw gakina awii'aa ima danakiiwin, "daa akiwenzim giginebekiwi! Giishpin zaaminad, zhigwa gabi-madiz."

Mii', nibyo aa'aag ima danakiiwin izhi madaabii'ad agamiing iwedi gaa gawishimo, gakina bakobii'ad ima nibi. Gakina awii'aa aakozi, gaa animakde o'odengwaa, onji aakozi-wad iwe giji-inaapinewin. Gakina mamoo bakobii'aad, gakina gaye mamoo'okoshkaa bagizo' ima, gakina mawi ozaam gakina daa ni-bo. Gakina zaaminaad iwi innini.

Mii iizhkwaaseg, iwi ininini ikido, "Giishpin ga awii'aa ayaasig, jitaa jimaaja'an." Daa gwaash-kwane, gii-kwaashkwebiigam zaswebi-iga'andage, bakobii ima nibi gaa ani ani-maadagaa. Gawiin geyaabi minowa gii waabi-mawsii. Mii' gakina awii'aa gaazaaminaad mii' giige. Endash ozaam iwi bawaajigan gaa ayaad iwe ikwe gaa bi waabimigood. Igiwi gaazaaminaasig, gaa izhi nibod.

Giizhaa iwedi jiibegamig, gii'izhinigo iwedi, besho ima Agawa Wiikwed. Aayawan waakaa'igansan iwedi igiwe gaa nibod. Nibiyo aaaag gii nibo, api gii zanaagad, za-naga'awag. Gaa ishpaanikewag, gaa biina'ajigzo inowaan wiiyawan ima biinj'aii. Gawiin be-bezhiig jina'in ozaam niibyo gii nibo, mii'iwi biinjwebin ayaad giiji-bagone'ag.

Mii' iwe gaa izhiseg, niiwaabidan iwe. Nii-waabidan gaye jiibegamigoon ayaagan. Mii' iwe gaa izhiseg, mii' apii iwe inini ani aanjised o'o ginebek, mii' iwa ikwe gaa aanjise'aad ino gaye bimaajitood odanakiiwin.

Sure enough, he noticed his legs started to turn black, they started to get little scales on them. His legs started to stick together, to rub against each other. Next thing you know, his legs started to form a tail, like a snake's tail. Pretty soon his whole bottom part of his body was a snake, and it was just swimming in the water.

He told his wife, "Go get everybody, tell them to come here. If they want to live, they have to touch me!" So, she did, she went there and told everybody in the village, "My old man has turned into a snake! If you touch him, then you'll live."

So, lots of people in the village came down to the beach where he was lying, they all went into the water. They were all sick, their faces were turning black, they were sick from the plague. They went in there and all waded together, they were all swarming amongst each other in there, all crying because they were going to die. They all touched that man.

When it was done, that man said, "If there's nobody left, I have to go." He made a jump, splash, into the water and swam away. They never saw him again. But everybody that touched him got cured. It was because of that dream he had of that woman that came to him. Those that didn't touch him, they died.

I went to that burial site, I was taken there, up by Agawa Bay. There are little houses there where those people died. Lots of people died, it was a tough, tough time for them. They dug a great big hole in the ground, and they just put the bodies inside there. They couldn't have individual burials because so many of them died, they had to throw them in a big hole.

That's what happened, I've seen that. I've seen where those graves were. That's what happened, that's when that man got turned into a snake, it was that woman that turned him into one, and he saved his village.

BAKEBII'IGAN NISWI

Megwaa aa'aag ezhise' indwa ginebekoog baataadowinan

Gii wiindamoninim miinowaa dibaajimowin gaa izhiseg, apii awii'aa aanjised o'o ginebek. Iwe gaa izhiseg mewinzhaa, ikidog iwedi endazhi' wiinde Ganabajing, miimaa onjibaayan, mii'ima aanji'an, endazhi' izhi wiinde Ishpagoodemag, iwe dibishkoo ishpi'ininaabik.

Gii ayaa ima oshkinins iwe ininaabik, wiinge mino miinikaa iwi. Mii' iwedi endizhi omda-mino, win gaye owiijiiwaagansan, niidabiwaad iwedi mawinzo'og, endizhi jiikikamigizi', baapiwiwad, babaa maajibimijiwebinaad asiniig. Gosha, wanishkwe'idiwad.

Gezika, gaa waabidan gegoo agawat'ii iwa ini-nabik, a'ii iwi otawagenz. Gaa mamaandaawi-jiged, "Wegonesh iwe?" Izhaad iwedi, giiayaa ima agaashiinyi ma'iinganens. Wiinawaa dowa, "Awnsaa, debidinada o'o ma'iingan!" Ezhi debidinagaad inowaan animoons gaye maaji odaminowad sa o'o. "Ambe giiwewi'inada!" Mii', gaa'izhhigewaad, giiwewi'inaan o'o ma'iingan.

CHAPTER THREE

When People Get Turned into Snakes by Consequence

I'm going to tell you another story of what happened, when somebody got turned into a snake. This happened a long time ago, they say that in a place called Ganabajing, which is where I'm from, there's a place called Ishpagoodemag, it's like a high rock.

There was a little boy playing on that rock, it was a good blueberry place. He was there playing, him and his little friend, sitting there picking berries, having fun, laughing, pushing rocks around. Y'know, causing a bit of a racket.

All of a sudden, they see something behind a rock, it was a little ear. They were curious, "What is that?" They went over there, there was a tiny little baby wolf. They're like, "Aw, let's grab this wolf!" They grabbed that little puppy and started playing with it. "Let's take this home!" So, they did, they took that wolf home.

Igiwe odaminoganawa ima wiigwaamiyan. Bezhiig iwe getaa
diziwad ikido, "Anaa, gawiiin iwe animoosh, a'a ma'iiganens
gosha. Aandi gaa-odinamiig iwe?" "Onh, giin odinanan iwedi
Ishpagoodemag! Mii'iwedi gaa aayaad." "Gii azhenigena!
Ayaa gosha gijiwaawendaagwad iwedi. Gegoonan iwedi
bimaadizi'inan gaa daawaad igiwe biinji'ininabikoog, gawiin
gegoo jibabaamendaman iwedi. Aaniish gaaizhijigewin iwedi?"
"Amanj... Gii'ashasanan."

Mii', azhaagiiwaad iwedi wajiw gaye iwe gaye ma'iiganens.
Jii'daashkikaa ima wajiw, mii' izhi wiinde "Daashkikaag." Mii
izaawad ima gaadaashkikaag, ozaam iwi gaadaashkikaag
ani niisaya'ii amigad mii' iwe ma'iiganens bangishin biinji'ii
gaawesaa jii'odaapinaad.

Misa ma'iiganens gaa nibo, sa nibod ima gaa dashkikaag. Mii
igi oshkininiseg gawiin gagoo wi'ikidosii'og, gawiin inendasi
ji'wiindemaa awii'aa ozaam ogikendaan gii onijiged. Mii'idash
giimiji izhi giwaad iwedi Ganabanjing, izhe gi-waad iwedi
danakiiwin.

Giwabang, gakina goshkozi. Wiinawaa izhinaagwad, "Onh,
ndaakoshkade, niiwiisagen-dam nimisad!" Gawiin awii'aa
gekendansiin wengonen, maagizhaa misad inapinewan?
Amang iidog? Maagizhaa gegoo ingii-amwaa? Mii'
apii, gawiin awii'aa gikenjigise wegonen onji'maazhise.
Ganawaabandanawad omisa-dani'aa gaye gegoo mamajise
bin-ji'omisadani'aa. Gakina igo danakiiwin bezhig-wan
inamanji'o, giji'zayegendaang gaa izhiseg.

Mii', gezika, bezhiig awii'aa bangishin gaye ojibinigoo.
Maajimamaadinaad ima mitakamig, aazhigwa gikendan
iwe wiiyaw maaji gi-ginebekiwi. Miinowaa bezhiig awii'aa
bangishin, miniowa bezhig awii'aa bangishin, minowa bezhiig
awii'aa bangishin.

They were playing with it in their wigwam. One of the Elders said, "Hey, that's not a dog, that's a baby wolf. Where'd you get that?" "Oh, we got that at Ishpagoodemag! That's where it was." "You put that back! That's a very sacred place. There're things that live inside those rocks, you're not supposed to bother anything there. What were you doing there?" "I don't know... We'll put it back."

So, they went back to that mountain with the baby wolf. There was a big crack in that mountain, they call that crack "Daashkikaag." They put that wolf in that crack, but that crack goes down and that baby wolf fell in there and they couldn't get it out.

That baby wolf died, it died in that crack. But the boys didn't want to say anything, they didn't want to tell anyone because they knew they'd made a mistake. So they just went back to Ganabajing, back to the village.

The next day, everybody woke up. They were like, "Oh, I got a stomachache, my stomach hurts!" Nobody knew why, was it a stomach flu? Who knows? Maybe something they ate? At that particular time, nobody knew what was wrong. They looked at their stomachs and you could see something moving inside their stomachs. The whole village was like that, it was pretty scary what happened.

Then, all of a sudden, one person fell down and started shaking back and forth. They started to wiggle around on the ground, next thing you know their body started to turn into a snake. Then another person dropped, then another person, then another person.

Mii gosha gekandan gakina awii'aa baabangishi-noog. iwe odoon. Gakina iwe danakiiwin, gegaa igo gakina, ginebekowi. Maaji izhinaagoziwinan giji'bikwaakod, iwi giji bikwaa ginebekoog maaji'inaawanidiwag inagakeyaa iwedi wajiw.

Mii iwedi gaa azhaad. Ginebekoog gaa baabang-ishinowad, misa ezhizhe zagaakwa'ad migo iwi doodamowad. Gegapii, angoseg biinji wajiw, mii' azhaad iwedi gaa daashkaag, Daash-kaabkaan. Gegaa gakina iwi danakiiwin gine-bigowi. Mii iwi gaa'izhiseg.

Gaa niizhiwag eta zhaabwii'ad. Igi niizh ikweg giiji-ikwe inaapine, mii'iwedi gaa'ayaad, zaagi-jiy'ii ima danakiiwin, gawiin igi gii'aazhoowayasii, gawiin ginebekowi'aa. Wi-inawa aazha gaa ginebekowi'ag. Igiwe Ikido gii'izhaad Wiiigwassensikaa-zaaga'igan, beshoo igo ima gaa ayaang. Iwedi ani azhaad Wiigwas-sensikaa-zaaga'igan dash wiindemaagawad gaa'izhiseg. Igi ikido "Giinawind gaa danakiiwin ginebekowi'ad."

Ayaa iwe baataadowinan izhaawad iwedi waawendaakaa endazhi', babaawanishkwenda ininaabikon gawise, awesiinsag odaapinidwa iwedi. Aapi gaa ayizhidaaniwan, gii gikendamin gaa jimigoshkaajiwang inowaan gegoon, on-ji'idim ji'izhaad aawii'aa iwedi ozaam eta gaa wi'izhad iwedi manidooke. Gawiin izhasii iwedi jiodaminowin.

Ini gaa aa'aad wiiyaw ayaawan iwedi wajiw. Ayaawan ini aa'aag okanan iwedi. Ayaa a'a baagwadinaa, gaye a'a misi-ginebek izhitaa i'i zaaga'iganiing iwedi. Mii', gaa Anishinabekewi, gigendamin aanid gaa'ayaagin gawiin giinawind iwe.

Next thing you know everybody was dropping. Snakes were coming out of their mouths. The whole village, almost all of them, got turned into snakes. They started to make a big ball, that great big ball of snakes started to travel towards that mountain.

That's where it went. Snakes were falling off, but they'd just get back on again. Finally, it disappeared into that mountain, it went into that crack, Daashkaabkaan. The whole village almost got turned into snakes. That's what happened.

There were only two survivors. There were two women that were on their menstrual cycle, they were on the outside of the village, they weren't affected, they never got turned into snakes. The rest of them were done. They say that they went to Birch Island, which is not too far from us. They went to Birch Island and told them what happened. They said, "Our village got turned into snakes."

There was a consequence for going to that sacred site, pushing rocks over, taking animals from there. When I was living in my community, we knew not to bother those things, that was a forbidden place to go to because you only went there to do spiritual business. You don't go there to play.

There are human remains also on that mountain. There are human bones there. There is also a cave, and a serpent that lives in that lake there. So, as Anishinaabek, we know that some of these places are not for us.

Eta aa'aag gaa-gikendaasowaad inake'ii iwe gegoo daa azhaa iwedi onji inakamigizi, Gawiin gaaginka awii'aa izhaasii iwedi, gawiin awii'aa memwech. Noongom ayaamagad waawendaakaa iwe, gaye gakina izhaa iwedi pitoonawad biiwaabikomiskwemeg gaye bezhigo-biiwaabikoonseg. Nishke aanind gegoonan igo boonanijiigaade.

Only people that are specially educated at that sort of stuff will go there for special reasons. Not everybody will go there, it is not for everybody. Today there is a sacred site, and everybody is going over there with their canned salmon and pennies. But some things are just meant to be left alone.

Apii misi-ginebekoog amo'ad aa'aag

Noongom niidibaajim apii misi-ginebek maaji oma' aa'aag gaye wegonen onji'oma'ad. Ikido'og gaa izhiseg iwe noomaya, mi'igo giji noonmaya naanwaak biboone. Inowaan min-jimendamowinan iwi gii izhiseg dibishiko bi-jinaago. Aaniin igo apii noodaman iwi dibaajimowin, mmi'igo dibizhkoo gaa izhiseg noomaya. Gi'daajimowaad iko iwi dibaajimowin, indigoko anitaagod dibishkoo noomaya.

Igiwe ikido mewinzha, gaa waabimaa a'a misi ginebek ima zaaga'iganiing. Iwe gaa mindimooyenh biinji'wiigiwaam, inaabi agami-ing, gaye waabidang inowen eshkanan aazhoged ima agaami-ziibi. Gii ayaa iko ima gete dana-kiiwin iwedi, Ginebigook Zhibiigaashwaad, iwi " babaagaa misi-ginebekoog ozhibii'ibendwa" iwi wenji danakiiwin izhi wiinde.

Gaa wasa ima iwedi miinowa ininabik, izhi wi-inde "Mendogwayaasag". Shke migo ima enda-zhi' iwe, mii iwedi o'o mindimooyenh ayaad. Mi'iwate inaabi agaami-ziibi, izhi wiinde en-dashi' "Naadawad".

Mii iwe memindage'aa endazhi', owaabidan inowaan aazhawaadagaa iwa eshkanan mii' wi-indamaw onabeman, "Niinabem, gegoo ayaamagad agwajiing magizhaa gaye daa gi inaab!" Zhamaag inaabi mii' gegat a'a giji-misi ginebek. Wiinge enigok inaabi, "Oonh, gegoo agwanendan!" Wigibidoone'idizo, "Shaa, awenen iwa? Iwe inini. Odaa ayaawan Inini dakwaneman!".

36

CHAPTER FOUR

When Serpents Eat People

Now I'm going to tell of when a serpent started to eat people and why they ate them. They say this happened in recent times, recent as in within the last 500 years. There are memories of this happening like it was yesterday. Whenever I hear this story, it's like it happened not too long ago. When they told this story, they made it sound like it was just a little while ago.

They say years ago, they seen a serpent in the lake. There was an old lady in her wigwam, she looked out at the lake, and she saw these horns going across the river. There used to be an old village there, Ginebigook Zhibiigaashwaad, the "Place Where the Serpents are Written" is what that village is called.

Not too far from there is another rock, it's called "Mendog-wayaasag." But right at the place there, is where the old lady was. She looked into the river; they call that place "Naadawad."

At that particular place, she's seen that thing swimming across with those horns and she told her husband, "Honey, there is something outside I think you need to see!" He looked right away and sure enough it was a big serpent. He looked really hard, "Oh, it has something in its mouth!" She covered her mouth, "Oh my god, who is it? It's a man. It has a man in it's mouth!"

Gakina ima danakiiwin gikenjigewa gegoo izhis-eg. Gaa
miiyawan agimawa, awenen ima ayaad, awenen giiwosed,
aande enzhi-gaa aazhaa? Awenen ima ayaasii? Mii'
giizhenindamowa iwe zagaswe'idiwa igi ininiwag ayaasii
ima, miiya-wan mii' apan. Gaa mikawaandamowa iwedi gaa
mitigookaa miikanawa gaa wiikaa ji waabidamowa gii ayaagan.
M'i-ginebek nangwana ogii damigowaad.

Mii', gaa mashkiki aa'aag gii nandomaw Jigegwa gikendamowa
wegonen gita amowaan-da. Gaa maajiba'iwe gegoo iwe,
gawiin gii daa naganasii iwe ozaam gakina gi bimaadiziwin
ayaamagad ima nibi.

Gawiin dibishko gashkitoonsii, gikendan, daa azha
Misskwatomina! Gawiin iwe api gaa izhi giizhigad. Mii'
gawesa jiigiimii'in o'o gegoo iwe. Miii', zagaswe'idiwad,
gaye debwetamoo ji ayaad Jiiskaan, ga'bimideg babagiwayaanegamig, gaa gwaya onendamo wegonen onji'izhiseg,
wegonen igi ininiwag onji amodaa.

Gaa nandomo o'o inini ji bi'izhijiiged. Ikido gi'agaashiinwi,
aapiji gete ayaad, gaye owiiwan owiiji'igoon. Biindigawad iwi
jiiskaan. Gii ikido iwe jiiskaan aa'aazhawibide, migo miinawa
iwe ga'bimideg babagiwayaanegamig, aa'aazhawibideg.

Shke zhigo, bi-zaaga'am nakwejigan goii ayaan. Ikido, "Iwe
ginebek gaa ani amogowin, gaye gawiin ji gibijiid baamaa
gakina awii'aa nibod. Gaa genage jiimaajiib'iwe iwe ozaam
gi-ji'mindido gaye gijizoongizi. Gii wiindema iwedi ji izhaan
Dikinaaganing, inowaan dikinaagan ini-naabikoog ishpiming
iwedi. Ayaa iwe agaashi-inyi awi'aa biinji iwe ininabik,"
Bagwagi-nini, iwe agaashiinyi awi'aa ezhinikaazo, iwe
agaashi-inyi bagoj bezhig. "Ni'izhaa iwedi gaye gaa ozhi-toon
bagijiganan o'o Bagwaji-nini, ini agaashi-inyi awi'aa, gaye
giishpin ji'nisaad ino ginebek."

Everybody in the village knew that something was happening. They did a body count, who's here, who's hunting, where did they go? Who's missing? It was determined at that council that several of the men were missing, their bodies were gone. They noticed in the trees there were pathways that they've never seen before. The serpent was eating them.

So, the medicine people were called upon to try to understand why they were being eaten. You can't run from something like that, you can't get away from it because your whole life is on the water.

It's not like you can, you know, go to Saskatoon! Not back in those days. There's just no way you can escape something like that. So, they had a council, and it was agreed to have a Jiiskaan, a Shaking Tent, to try to figure out what happened, why these men were being eaten.

They called upon a man to come and do this. They say he was small, he was very old, and his wife would help him. They went into that lodge. They say that the Shaking Tent was going back and forth, back and forth.

Sure enough, he came out with the answer. He said, "The snake is eating us, and it won't stop until everybody's dead. We can't run from it as it is too big and too strong. I've been told to go up to Dikinaaganing, those cradle rocks up there. There's a little person inside that rock," Bagwaji-nini, is that little person's name, the Little Wild One. "I'm going to go there and make offerings to Bagwaji-nini, the little person, and see if they can kill that snake."

Mii' gaa'izhigaad, gii izha iwedi Dikinaaganing, iwe ininaabik. Gaa aadoon anind bagijiganan iwedi. Gii maaji ganonaa ino ininaabik, "Baaki-nan a'a niin, igiwe nwiji aa'aag nibowin. O'o ginebiek gaa amogonan gakina awi'aa! Gii ayaa giji zoongizi, giin eta wenji-bimaaji'ang!"

Gezika, baakise iwi ininaabik. Gii ayaa ima agaashiinyi awi'aa biindig, oshki-aa'aa. Iwe mashkikinini wendamowa gakina gegoo gaa agaaashiinyi awi'aa gakina gegoo. Ikido, "Nwiji'aa'aag zegiziwe. Niibomin, gii minin ino nimiigiwenan." Bagwji-nini ikido, "Ni'odaapinen inowaan miigwiwenan. Shke waabidan nibikwakan, Wenge nita bimoojige, waabidan ni'mitigwaabiig. Niodaapinan iwi onjishkaawaaniwe."

Bagwaji-nini aazhoobatoo igiwe ininaabikoog, Dikinaaganing, izhi gwaashkwanid binji'ii Naadawad. Migo biinji ima bezhigiwan endazhi'. Gezika, nibi maaji zawegiiga, babaa aa'aazhawibide, aa'aazhawibide.

Gezika, miskwe maaji biizitaaga ishpa, mii' i'i misi-ginebiek agomod ima ishpa nibi. Bagwaji-nini zaagiji'gwaashkoni onibikwakan gaye omitigwaabiig izhikidod, "Gii nisa iwe ginebek." Mii' izhi diaabajimod, "Gii nisa i'i ozaam gii andawendan eshkanan, mii' o'oodemag gaa naazikagowa gishpin ozhitoonsii gii bagijgenan.

"Iwe onji'iwe nisaad igiwe ininiwag ozaam gi-inowa gawiin gii izhitoonsii ini bagijigenan, mii' maaji ozhitoonwa ine. Bijiinag daa gii odaapinaa igiwe abinoonjiinyag, aapiji gizhawen-daagozim."

That's what he did, he went up to Dikinaaganing, that rock. He put some offerings there. He started to talk to that rock, "Open up for me, my people are dying. The snake will eat all of us! You're so powerful, you're the only one that can save us!"

All of a sudden, that rock opens up. There was a little person in there, a young person. That medicine man told that little person everything. Said, "My people are scared. We're dying. I give you these gifts." Bagwaji-nini said, "I accept these gifts. Look at my arrows, I am very good at shooting, look at my bow. I will take on the challenge."

Bagwaji-nini ran across those rocks, Dikinaaganing, and jumped right into Naadawad. Right into that spot. All of a sudden, the water started to splash, going back and forth, back and forth.

All of a sudden, blood started to bubble up, and that Serpent laid there on top of the water. Bagwaji-nini jumped out with his arrows and his bow and said, "I killed that snake." But he also told them, "I killed it because I wanted the horns, but it's family will come back for you if you don't make your offerings.

"The reason why it was killing those men was because you weren't making your offerings, so it started to take them. Pretty soon it was going to take the children, you're very lucky."

Igi aa'aag ima ga'ayad danakiiwin jiikendamoog gaye wii-makawaamaa ozhitoodaad bagijiganan. Iwi misi-ginebek iwedi gaaizhi mooshka`agonjin iwi minis. Izhinakaademowed "Nibwaakaa Min-is." Mii'ima moozhka'agon. Ini aa'aag izhaad misi-ginebek abid, azhaa eshkanan apan ozaam iwi ga'agaaashiinyi azhaa odaapina'a. Obi-igozhanan iwi mis-ginebek miziwe igo omisa-dang.

Odaapinemowad iwe miskwi ino misi-ginebek maaji zhizhoobii'aad gaa izhisegm Geget maaji zhizhoobii'gaad ino misi-ginebek, niimida-ginwaabigozid iwi misi-ginebek ima ininaabik iwi omiskwiim. Mii' gosha ezhi-wiinde iwe gete danakiiwin Ginebigook Zhibiigaashwaad, iwi "gaa endazhi' o'o misi-ginebekoog gii mazinibaganjigan i'i ininaabikoog." Mii' iwe mazinibaganan ezhi ayaad, aapiji gosha giji waawendaakaa endazhi'.

Niwiji aa'aag gaa makawaamaa apiiji-enandaagwad bagijigenan ayaagan. Gabaa-nadomin gaa izhi bimaadiziwi ima aki, ini ziibi-ing gaye ini zaaga'iganan bizhishig igo bagi-jigenan. Ini aki bagosendan gizhewaadizibin ini bagosendan nitaa izhijigem aazhoo miigiwem. Gishpin izhijigesii iwi, gaa nibowin gakina, gawi-in ezhi gawedwe.

The people in the village were happy and thankful, they were reminded to make their offerings. That Serpent washed up on this island, they call it "Nobel Island." It washed up there. The people went there to that Serpent, the horns were already gone because that Little Person took them. But they cut that Serpent open all down its stomach.

They took the blood of that Serpent and painted what happened. They actually painted that Serpent, a forty foot Serpent on the rock with that blood. That's why they call that old village Ginebigook Zhibiigaashwaad, the "Place Where Serpents are Painted on Rocks." That's why those pictographs are there, it's a very sacred place.

My people were reminded how important offerings were. We cannot live our life on the land, the rivers and the lakes without our offerings. The land insists upon generosity, it insists upon a constant giving back. When we don't do that, we will die, there's no question.

MJsi-ginebekoog migiwe ini aa'aag gaa makawaamaa

Mii' naagaj bezhigiwan ima endazhi', iwi bezhigwan danakiiwin, niwiji'aa'aa waniikewa miinawaa. A'a niizh ininiwag daa izhi bagizo' ima ziibiig. Gaa wiindamaw, "Gego bagizo'gaan iwedi, ayaa misi-ginebek waanikaan iwedi." Mii' gaa izhi misawendamowad jizhijiged. Gii izhise iwi nimishoomis gi ayaa iw apii.

Igiwe niizh ininiwag misawendan ji'izhijige iwa. Gaa izhi bagiso ima, bezhig iwi ogi ayaan moodaabik. Gegona, gikendan ani gii moosh-kinejiwanen iwi moodaabik ginege awii'aa gii bizindawasi, "Onh, gawiin gego ima, gaa gegoo niisayi'ii iwedi! Ni'andawendamin ji'bagizo' ima, gego win-damoshikan izhidjige gaa ayaan ." Gigekkandan, maashkwezi animo bengiins shkwa minikwen moodayaabik.

Shke dash, wii begizo' iwedi baawitidoong, aa-zhawadagaad. Gezika iwa gaabishagiishkaanded, mii' gogid anaamiindim gawiin jimookibii. Iwi biisitaagan mookii biijinag gii giishkawa gogiid, giji'biisitaagan, wenge maazhimagod.

CHAPTER FIVE

Serpents Give the People a Reminder

But sometime later at that same spot, that same village, my people forgot about that again. There were two men that were swimming on that river. They were told, "don't swim there, there's a serpent hole there." But they wanted to do it. This happened in my grandfather's time.

Those two men wanted to do it. They were swimming in there, one of them had a mickey. Only, you know when you're all mickey'd up you don't want to listen to nobody, "Oh, there's nothing here, there's nothing down there! We want to swim here, don't tell us what to do." You know, get all tough after you have a little bit of mickey.

Sure enough, they're swimming down those rapids, going back and forth. All of a sudden that real dark one, he goes down and he never came up. This bubble came up after him after he went down, a great big bubble, and it stunk.

Owiijiiwaaganan gii zegizi. Ikido, "Ziihay, gawi-in! Aaniish
gaa izhised niwiijiiwaagan?" Mii' ezhi jibebizo. Gibezhigwan
minowa, gawiin jimookibii, eta bezhiig giji'biisitaagan. Biinish
iwi biisitaagan mooshka'agonjin. Gii baakise, gaye gaa izhi
bagiji' wiinge gimaanzhimaagwad. I'i aashimaagoog gegaa
nibowin wiiyawan, mii' gaa ikido. Gii angosewag; igi niizh
ininiweg gii angosewaf.

Awii'aa onzaabi waasa gaye ogiwaabidan gaa'izhijiseg. Shke,
iwi nandomaw o'o mashkiki aa'aa jibi izhaa, mii' gaa ayaad
manidookewin wiigaagikendamo gaa izhiseg.

Mii' ingwana iwi misi-ginebek. Ikido iwi misi-ginebek
opaapina' igi ininiwag ozaam gaa gi'izhitoosii inowaan
bagijiganan. Giwanikemin, gikendamin iwi, ozaam
giwanikemin, mii' ingwana igi ininiwag onji aapidendi. Gagwe
bizhawenaa.

Mii', ima iwe jiiskaan, ogii gegwa nakomaan ino misi-ginebek.
Ikido iwi misi-ginebek, "Gaa bi azhena bezhiig giiwena, mii'
niin ganawenima, iwe makadewizi, niin igo." Mii' gaa izhizeg,
iwedi wiiyaw moozhka' ima agamiing.

Ayaa mitigoonsan ziindaakoshinoon biinji'otawagan, niizh
mitigoonsan biinjini ojaanin. Biinjidoon ini giji makade
ininaabik. Gi'ayaa ini waabigan, waabigan, ziinji'agoke
oshkiinzhigoon. Ikido onji' iwa miiyaw wenji izhijigaazo inake
mii' daa wiindamaagesii gaa waabidang gemaa gaanoondang,
mii' daa gaa giigidod. Igi aa'aag makawaamaa minowaa iwi
jeta ozhijigedawan bagijigenan o'o aki. Mi'iwa gaa izhiseg.

His partner got scared. Said, "Oh, no! What happened to my friend?" So, he dove in. Same thing, he never came back up, just one great big bubble. When that bubble hit the top of the water it just opened, and it released a very stinky smell. It smelled almost like dead bodies, that's what they say. They disappeared; those two guys disappeared.

Somebody was watching from a distance and had seen what happened. So, they called a medicine person to come, and they had a ceremony to try and find out what had happened.

It was the Serpent. He said the Serpent took those men because we weren't making our offerings. We forgot, we knew this, but we forgot, and now these men are gone. I'll try to get them back.

So, in that shaking tent, he tried to negotiate with that Serpent. But the Serpent said, "I'll bring one back, but I'll keep the other one, the black one, for myself." That's what happened, the other body washed up on shore.

It had sticks wedged in its ears, two sticks going up its nose. In its mouth there was a great big black stone. There was clay, waabigan, jammed in its eyes. They say the reason why the body was prepared like that was so that it wouldn't tell what it has seen or heard, so that it wouldn't be able to talk. Our people were reminded again that you have to make your offerings to the land. That's what happened.

Nimishoomis gii gwiiwizensi apii iwi gii izhiseg, gaa ezhi'inig iwedi endazhi'. Giwiindema gakina o'o debajimowin. giwiindema mii' iwa gaa'izhiseg. Ikido, "Ngi'wiijindoo na-naandawi'ige, gegwa makwa ino miiyawan" Aanissh inaa ini makawaamaa igi aa'aag jeta ap-ane bezhigwan inowaan wii bagigigenan iwi misi-ginebek.

Onh enyanh, wii gaa'bemaaji'igonan, zhigo gaa odaapinegonan giishpin gwayak izhi-jigewin. Nimamaakwendan iwi noongom, gii gwayak izhigigemin noongom inake bezhigwan iwi nibikaa?

Iwe nakwetaw gaa mawiin gawwiin. Aabiji naanaagadawenima nidaanis, aabiji naanaagadawenima geg aanikoobijiganag. Gii apiji'ishpendaagwad ezhi naadiziwin gaa ezhi minigoziwin moozhag igo ezhi gash-kidtoonwi mii' Aki aa'aag miinowa.

Aapii, gii aa'aag apiji nonde wayezhingen-iniwad, indawaaj nonde wayeshingewad. Dibishko inaakigewinensan gaawesaa wenji bimaajiing, ashoojisiganan gaa ogii wiji'igosii, wayeshingwinan gaa ogii wiiji'igosii. Inowaan gaa manidookeng, gii izhi bimaadizin, gaa wii-jigaabawitaadiwin iwi nibi, igo misi-ginebekoog, igiwe gakina gaa aya'aad. Mi'iwe gaa ezhi bimaaji'ing

My grandfather was a boy when this happened, and he took me to that spot. He told me the whole story, he told me this was what happened. He said, "I was part of the search party, I was trying to find those bodies." That's a reminder to people that we have to be consistent with our offerings to the Serpent.

So yes, they can save us, but they can also take us if we don't act right. I think about that right now, are we acting right now in a way that is consistent with our waters?

The answer is probably no. I keep thinking about my daughter, I keep thinking about future generations. It's really important for us to go back as much as we can to be Earth people again.

Right now, our people are very political, they're extremely political. It's like policies ain't gonna save us, frameworks ain't gonna save us, politics ain't gonna save us. It's our ceremonies, it's our way of life, it's our relationship with the water, the serpents, with all those beings. That's what's going to save us.

Amanisookaade Danakiiwin

Gii dgibaajimadoon iwi amanisokaa gegoo gaa izhise ima ndanakiwwin. Gii izhiseg geg niizhwaak shaa niishtana baboon; migo apii midaaswaak shaa zhaangaswaak biboon.

Igiwe ikido iko aa'aag jiikeyawa gaye ima izhitwaad ima danakiiwiin, o'o danakiiwin mii' gibezhigwan gaa gidazhindaman aazhigo, iwe danakiiwin ezhi'winde Ginebigook Zhi-bi'gaazhwat.

Ayaawan ino mazinibii'iganan igiwe misi-ginebekoog, giji gete danakiiwin, o'o gete danakiiwin izhi'winde. Mi'ima gaa daawad. Mii', iwi dibaajimowin ge gi'izhiseg iwedi gaye wegonen niji aa'aag gii'izhi aanjigozid sa endazhi' iwedi endazhi' noongom aayaad.

Giji-gigizheb aabiding, aa'aag onishkaaw, aa'aag maaji dozhiitawaad ji daa anakamigizi, awii'aa izhi mikawaabidan gegoo. Aapii aayaad iwedi agwajiing ginibinaadid, bekobina'aa ini akikoon ima agamiin, mii' maaji bimiwidoon iwedi o'mitigowaakaaigan. Gaa mikawaabidaw gegoo maamakaaj, gegoo apiji maamakaaj'ayi'ii.

Gaa mikawaabidan a'a iwedi ininaabik, giji-ininaabik, gegaa igo ninj inigokwaa, ogijayi'ii ima waakaaigan. Iwi ikwe mikawaabidan iwe; ikido, "Wegonen o'o ininaabik onji-aabid ima ogijayi'ii nwaakaaigan? Igiwe abinoojiingyag maawiin wedaminowad."

CHAPTER SIX

Haunted Village

I'm going tell you about a ghostly thing that happened in my village. It happened about 120 years ago; it was somewhere in the early 1900s.

They say that the people were happy and that they lived in this village, the village was the same village that I talked about before, the village was called Ginebigook Zhibii'gaazhwat.

There are pictographs there of serpents, it's a historical village, an old village they call it. That's where they lived. So, this story is about what happened there and why my people relocated from that site to the site where we are now.

Early one morning, people were getting up, people were getting ready to do their chores, and somebody noticed something. When they were outside to go get water, they would put their bucket in the lake, and they started to carry it back to their little cabin. They noticed something peculiar, something very strange.

They noticed that there was a rock, a big rock, almost bigger than my hand, it was on top of the house. A woman noticed that; she said, "Why is that rock on top of my house? Those kids are probably playing around."

Giwaabang nibinaadid. Megwa gii giiwedo, ogi mikawaabiman minowaa giji-ininaabikon ogija-yi'iing. Ezhi wiindamowa onabaman, "Geg, maajaan ishpiming izhaan naazikwe igi ininaabikoog. Igiwe anind abinoojiingyag daa izhi odaminwaa igi innaabikoog."

Mii', sago gaa izhijiged, debibina midaasan mii' mooshkinebii'ad mashkosiwan. Ogi ozhi'aan giji zeginaagozi gaa izhi asaad jigayiii waakaa'igan enandam ji zegi'ad igiwe abinoojingyag.

Gii waabang, ishpan winibinaadid, bi'aazhegiwe, gaa'izhe mikawaabimad ini ini-naabikood ogijayi'ii waakaa'igan, mii' noowaj gii nimindido igi ininaabikoog. Iwi gaa zeginaagozi midaas gagenage jii'zegoziwad wengonan igo o'o jimaajaa.

Mii', wiindamowad onaabemaan, "Ninaabem, aniish inaa izhiwebag? Wengonen igi ite ini-naabikoog abi'iad ogijayi'ii waakaa'igan?"

"Gawiin gikendaaziing." Wiin igo dibishkoo, "Amanj igo." Mii', ezhi'ishpaandawed ima waakaa'igan gaye naazikawad igi. Gii mindidowag, ge igi gaa mindido bezhigwan okosimaanag!

Giwaabang agwagiing izhaa nibinaadid minawaa, bi-ezhagiwe gimikawaabidang ima ogijayi'll waakaa'igan ayawan ima neyaabikoonsag, gi'ayabi mindidowa apiij okosimaanag, wenge giji-mindidowa. Gii zegize, ezhi wiindamowa onaabemaan, "Gegoo maazhise, Aaniish igi ini-naabikoog ishpiming ayaad? Wenge gosha giji-mindidowag."

The next day she went to go get her water. When she was walking back to the house, she noticed that there was another big stone up there. So, she told her husband, "Go up there and get those stones off. Some of those kids are playing with stones."

So, what she did was, she grabbed a pair of pants and she filled them with grass. She made it look real scary and she put it by the house thinking that it was going to scare those kids.

The next day, she went up to go get water, she came back, and she noticed that those stones were on the house, but they were bigger. Those scary pants never scared whatever it was away.

So, she told her husband, "Honey, what the hell is going on? Why are there stones on top of the house?"

"I don't know." He's like, "Beats me." So, he went back up that house and got them off. They were big, they were as big as pumpkins!

The next day she went out to get water again, she came back and noticed that on top of the house there were small boulders, they were even bigger than pumpkins, they were big. She got scared. She told her husband, "Something's wrong. How did those stones get up there? They're too big."

Mii', babaa'izhaa imaa danakiiwin, maajaa gaa ganoona'
igi aa'aag, "Gegoo izhiwebed ima, wengoneniish ayaad
giji-ininaabikoog ogijayi'ii niwaakaa'igan?" Gii maaji ikido
gebezhigwan, "Shke nimikawaanan ininaabikoog ogijayi'ii
nii-waakaa'igan ge. Nimikawaanan imaa ishkwe'ii aajigitigaan,
nimikawaanan ima nigitigenwinan igo giji-ininabikoog miziwe.
Amanj igo ima onji aayaad."

Gii waabang, iwe gidimaagi'aa ikwe, gii nan-dawaaganjige
ima owaakaa'igan. Ezhi mika-waabidan ima giji mayagi'ag.
Ezhi mikawaabi-mad iwe bii-akakanzhens, miskwa akakanzhe.
Obijimaandan,bijimaate gegoo jaagaakidene. Ayaawan ima
aagaashiinwi akakanzhenseg, biiindig waakaa'igan. Miish igo,
ezhi zaagiji'na', ezhi mayagenda, "Wegonen igi akakanzhenseg
aayaad ima? Aakaa aaniin dena onji'izhiseg?"

Naagaj gii-ishwaa-naawakweg. Iwedi waakaa'igan giji
bashkinewa. Aagaashiinwi aka-kanzhenseg maaji mookise
miziwe wenge gaa maazhimagwad. Gezika, gaa biijimaate
miziwe iwi danakiiwin, wenge maazhimagwad.

Mii' geget, gaa aazha gekenda'agwan gegoo maazhiseg.
"Wengonen igwe akakanzhens, igi gizhideweg akakanzhen,
ezhe babaamika-waandwa ande igo giimooj abi'aad ima
waakaa'igan? Gaa ogikenjigesi ezhiseg omaa nii' gegoo apiji
giji zegendaagwad izhiseg."

Neshka, gaa izhi gaganoonawad igi giji-aa'aag, gaye giji-aa'aag
ikido, "Gegoo igo iwi, gegoo igo gijimaazhise. Mii' eta iwiw
danakiiwin jii aan-jigoziwi, amanisookaade. Iwe danakiiwin
gakina gaa giido. Gaa giimooji'ayaa gegoowan ezhiseg."

So, she went around the village, she started talking to people, "Something's going on here, how come there's big stones on my house?" They started to say the same thing, "Well we found stones on our house too. We're finding them in our backyard, we're finding them in our gardens, we're finding these big stones everywhere. We don't why they're there."

The next day, that poor woman, she was digging around in her house. She noticed something very peculiar. She noticed that there was a little piece of coal, red coal. She could smell it, she smelled something burning. There were little coals in the house. So, she just put them out, she was wondering, "Why are these coals here? What the hell is going on?"

Later that afternoon, that house was just full of smoke. Little coals started to appear all over the place and it stunk. All of a sudden, the smell came over the village, and it stunk.

So of course, they knew something was wrong. Why were those coals, those hot coals, being found in mysterious places in the house? She didn't know. So she told her husband, "I don't know what's going on here but something very, very scary is happening."

So, they talked to the Elders, and the Elders said, "Something is up, something is very wrong. We have to move the village, it's being haunted. The whole village is talking. Mysterious things are happening."

Bezhig awi'aa oshkwaandem, goshkoziwi bishizhig
ishkwaandem mii' apan, gaa wiikaa jimaakaamowad o'o
ishkwaandem. Igiwedi ji maakaamowa waasejiganan
odaapinegadanan agoodegin ini mitigoog. Nibiyo igo gegoo
izhis-eg. Aa'aag owaakaa'iganan maaji zakidegin, giimooj
na'egaaj.

Mii', igi giji aa'aag, inandanmowa gaa onizhishinzinoon
ima endazhi'ing ima ge'aabi, gegoo wanishkwe'aa, gegoo
maazhise. Mii'gaa ogii gekandasii azhigo iwedi ayaa iwi o'o
oshkinins gi'izhinaa gaa igoshimod, gaye izhinind ji igoshimo
ima Ginebek Nayaashiing, Ginebek Nayaashiing wiinde.

Nitam-giizhigad gii asiind ji'igoshimo odedewin ikido,
"Gii ga'ayaa ima. Gii ga'ayaa ima bamaa odisiyagowin gi
izhinamowin." A'ii eta minaa waabooyaans, mii' eta i'i.
Gaa izhi giizhigad api gii zoongiz, mii' eta iwa gaminigowin
waabooyaan. Gaa igi miinigose babagi-wayaanegamigon
gaye apishimon gaye, gigekendan ina, gakina igo
nibaamashkimodan gaye gii'apishimowinan mizi gegoowan
naasaab. Gaa izhi giizhigad api gaa igoshimowin, gii igo-shimo
ozaam gii zoonigiz, gi'anishinaabewi.

Gaa minaa o'o oshkinins waabooyaans ini odede'in ezhi
wiindamagod, "Gii ga'ayaa ima baamaa ayaan izhinamowin."
Aazha niso-giizhik gii'izhise. Ini gaa odede bi'izhaa gaye
bi'waabima, "Gi'ayaan ina gii izhinamowin?

"Gawiin, genega gi'ayaasiin."

"Onh, mizi ima gi'ndanaadiziwin ge'ayabins." Miinaa bangii
nibi, miinaa ini bangii miijim gaa niso-gizhikag.

Ishkwaa nanogoon, ini gaa odede gii bi'izhigiwe. "Aaniin
nanda? Gi'ayaan awe izhinamowin?"

One person's door, they woke up and the whole door was gone, they never found the door. Others were finding windows that were taken out and they were hanging in the trees. Lots of things were happening. People's houses were being started on fire mysteriously.

So, the Elders, they decided it's not right to stay here anymore, something was disturbed, something's wrong. But what they didn't know was that previously there was a young boy that was put out to fast, and he was put out to fast at Ginebek Neyaashiing, Snake Point.

First day he was out to fast his dad told him, "You stay out here. You stay out here until you get your vision." All they gave him was a little blanket, that's it. Back in those days you were tough, that's all you got was a blanket. You didn't get tents and foamies and, you know, all sorts of sleeping bags and your pillows and all that stuff. Back in those days when you fasted, you fasted because you were tough, you were Indian.

They gave that boy a little blanket as his dad told him, "You stay out here till you get your vision." Three days passed. The dad came and seen him, "Did you get your vision?"

"No, I never got it."

"Oh, well you have stay out here a little longer." Gave him a little bit of water, gave him a little bit of food on the third day.

After five days, the dad came back. "How you doing? Did you get your vision?"

Gawiin, gaa mashi, genega mashi gii izhinamowin."

"Mii', gaa ndanaadiziwin ima igo ge'ayabins."

Iwe odede ge'izhigiwe azhi niizhwaasogonagad. Mii'
enizhegewed ini oshki-ininis mii' apan. Mii' gaa wiikaa gii
makwasii o'o oshkinins, ani babaa nandone'a , mii apiitendi.
Owaabooyaans ogoode izhpaatigoon. Gaa dibasadamowad
gaa'izhisegwan iwedi neyaashi.

Mii', megwaa izhiseg iwe, ima danakiiwin gaa odede
bi'niisaakiwe gaye ezhi mitinad iwe maawanji'idiwad gaa izhi
wiindamowa, "Ningosiz apiitendi, gii izhinanan jii igoshimod,
mii' apiitendi." Shke geget, gakina igi ima danakiiwin gaa
wenaanimizid, gii gwe mika-wa'an awe oshkininis, mii
gaawesa.

Bezhigwan apii, gakina gegoo ani amanisookaa-de. Mii'
inandanmowa nenaandoma anid awii'aa gaa mikawi o'o
ozhkinins. Daa inendam nandoma iwe inini izhi wiinzo
Giwegoom. Gi-wegoomm gaa wenge maaandaawizi ikido,
"Ngekandan gaa izhised iwi oshkininis. O'o oskininis mii'apane.
Ima endaadizid nibi noonbom, gii'waabima."

Geget, gikendan, gakina danakiiwin ozhiwan-iked mii' ani
maajaawad iwi endazhi' nanaan-donamaagewin gaa oshki
izhitaawa, anid aa'aag ima niisaaki waabiyog gaa waabimaad
o'o osh-kininis ima aayaad iwi misi-ginebek opikwa-nang.
Niisaa'ii izhaa gaye angose ima nibi.

O'o oshkininis owiijii'aan iwi misi-ginebek. Shke, igiwe
gaa gikendan iwe oshkininis ayaa ginwenzh iwedi geggo
gwayakasinoon. Mii', gaa aanjigozi iwe danakiiwin, aaniish
gaye mii'' ma aayaag iwe danakiiwin noongom. Mii' iwi gete
danakiiwin, giyaabi amanisookaade.

"No, I never got it, I never got my vision."

"Well, you have to stay out here a little bit longer."

The dad went back after seven days. When he went back, the boy was gone. They never found that boy, they looked for him, he was gone. His blanket was hanging up in the tree. They don't know what happened to him at that point.

So, while this was happening, in the village the dad came down and caught them in that meeting and told them, "My son is missing, we put him out to fast, but he's gone." So of course, the whole village was in panic, they tried to find that boy, but they couldn't.

At the same time, everything was being haunted. It was decided to call in some people that might be able to find that boy. I believe that they called in a man by the name of Giwegoom. Giwegoom was very spiritual and said, "I know what happened to that boy. That boy is gone. He's living in the water now, I've seen him."

Of course, you know, the whole village was packing up and as they were leaving that site to go find a new place to live, some people on the hill looked down and they seen that boy on the back of that Serpent. He went down and disappeared into the water.

That boy is with that Serpent. So, they knew that the boy was out there too long, that something wasn't right. So, they had to relocate the whole village, and of course they moved the village to where it is now. But the old village, it's still haunted.

Mii' giyaabi amanisookaade, shke gii dibaajimon wengonen onji amanisookaade. Ozaam nii gi'amanis iwedi. Aabiding nanaandomoon-zweban mii' inendaman, nii azhagiwe iwedi. Ayaa iwe ginoozh bimose, iwe gaa ginowaa gii ezhi'igwe mita'adoo iwedi.

Geg gikendan, ni'oshki ayaa apii, gaye ni'mooshkine iwe zhigiwin gaye zhiiwaaboo. Nashke, inandaman ji izhi'igewi iwedi. Ndayaa imaa iwi ininaabik besho gete danakiiwin gaye eta gii noondam ini, "Hisht!" gaa izhi ina waabi'an endash gii aayaa iwe inini iwedi. Shke, inendaman, onishishin awi'aa ayaa iwedi. Mii' wiinawaa eta ani maajaawa gaye niin bakaan ani maajaa'an, miii' anooj biinaad.

Mii' gi'izhgiwe gaa agaasen ni'babagiwayaanegamig, gi'ayaan nanaandawas-inii abagiwayaanegamigs, gaa badakisidoon ima mashkiigoon. Mii', ninamadab iwedi giji-gigizheb, nibaazaabidan iwi mashkiigoon eta ayaan giji bekaadizi'an, gawesa jii ozhitoon om-biigwe maagizha gaawiin gegoo. Mi'eta osha-bidaaman gegoo jimajise ima mashkiigoon.

Gezika, nibijimandan mayagi'maagwad. Ngigwe-kigaabawi dash iwi agaasen jiibaakwe-gizhaabikizigan gaa gi'ayaan binji iwedi, migo wewenge gwekisin. Gikendan apii biindigewin gaa babagiwayaanegamig iwe gizhaabikizigan biidaasamasin iko, maagizhaa gaye inaasamasen, gikendan, ga'ayaad awii'aa gaa gashkitoo iwe aabajidood.

Onh gizhaabikizigan wenge gwekisin, gaye i'i ishkwaandem igi biidaasamasin iwi babgi-wayaanegamigwegin. Inowaan ni'bimaadagaaziiwakizinan gigakizinen dezhi-ningidegan wenge gaye maanzhimaagwadoon. Inowaan ni'makizinan, mii gibiindige'an inowaan gaa ayaan. Iwi mii ningidegan!

It's still haunted, and I'll tell you why it's still haunted. Because I got haunted there. One time I was going to go moose hunting and I thought, I'll go back there. It's a long walk, it's a long hike back there.

But you know, I was young, and I was full of piss and vinegar. So, I decided to go back there. I'm on this rock near that old village and all I heard was, "HEY!" I looked and there was a man there. So, I thought, that's pretty cool there's somebody out here. So, they kinda went their way and I went my way, and it was kinda neat.

So I go back to my tent, I had a little prospector's tent, and I had it set up at this muskeg. So, I sat there early in the morning, I'm staring at this muskeg just being very patient, not even making a noise or nothing. Just looking for the slightest movement in that muskeg.

All of a sudden, I can smell something weird. I turned around and the little cook stove that I had in there, it was completely turned the other way. You know when you walk into a little tent your stove is facing you usually, or it's facing, you know, where a person can get at.

The stove was completely turned around, and the door was facing the canvas, and my rubber boots were on there just melting and they just stunk. Those were my boots, that's what I walked in there with. They were melted!

Mii', ni'maanminonendan giji weiib gaa aman-isoowan, mii' gaa izhi biindaakoojige'an. Wewiib gi'odapinan iwe gizhaabikizigan, mii ngizaagijiwebinan. Gii zaagi'am ima. Gi'dakobidoon nibabgiwayaan, Gii ayaan babigiwayaan gii dashkibidoon, gaa izhi dakobi-doo'an nizidan, mii' gii sagijibimoseyan ima ozaam gekendan amanisoowan. Ganika waniikesii iwe.

Iwedi gete akiwenzii, Kzhaazhowin, mi'iwe gaa ikido, "Ayaawag aa'aag ima inaadiziwad iwedi giyaabi, amanisookewa. Nibiyo aayaawag manidoowag iwedi ozaam gaa izhised iwe osh-kininis." Mii' iwi gaa izhiseg. Mii', iwi dana-kiiwin aanjigoziwad ozaam igiwe misi-genebekoog, ozaam amanisookewinan iwedie gaa dizhiseg.

O'o dawaa iwedi giji dani'aa ozaam igi misi-ginebekoog inaadizi inowaan izhiigewen'aa iwedi, wenge zhwaabi'aad ini izhiigewenan izhi-jigadagan. Ima zaagiiwan, ezhi wiinde Zaa-gidowaad, iwe bagoneyaa iwedi. Iskatemagad ezhi mooshkamon mi'iwe endazhi' wiinde Mindegweyasing.

So, I realized very quickly that I was being haunted, so I put my tobacco down. I quickly grabbed that stove, and I threw it out. I got out of there. I tied my shirt, I had a shirt on I ripped it in half, and I tied it on my feet, and I walked out of there because I knew I was being haunted. I'll never forget that.

That old man, Kzhaazhowin, he's the one that said, "There's people that live back there still, it's haunted. There's lots of spirits back there because of what happened to that boy." So that's what happened. So, the village got relocated because of serpents, because of hauntings that took place.

That area there is very rich because the serpents live in the tunnels there. It's fascinating how those tunnel systems work. At the mouth of the river, they call that Zaagidowaad, there's a hole there. It goes down and it comes up and a place they call Mindegweyasing.

Iwe izhiigewen iskate miinowaa, mooshkamo baakaan
iwedi gaa ayaag danakiiin iwa, Gine-bigook Zhibii'gaashwat.
Miinowaa iskatemagad, mooshkamong iwedi Ginebek
Neyaashing.

Mii' iwi izhiigewen iskatemagad geyaabi aabid-ing mii
mooshkamon iwedi Mnidoo Mnising. Iskatemagan miinowaa,
mooshkam iwedi Asi-niswaasning. Iwi izhiigewen mii aabi-
mamaajiseg, mii go aabi-mooshkamong. Aande igo apii
iwi izhiigewen mooshkamod mii ima giwiji aa'aag ezhaad
ishpiwedi ezhi igoshimowa ima. Mii gaye ima gewaabidaman
mazinibii'iganan, ozaam gaganoonag igiwe manidoog, iwi misi-
ginebekoog.

That tunnel goes down again, it comes up at another place where the village is, Ginebigook Zhibii'gaazhwat. Then it goes down again, it comes back up at Ginebek Neyaashiing.

Then that tunnel goes back down one more time and it comes back up at Mnidoo Mnising. Then it goes down again, comes up at Asiniswaasining. The tunnel just keeps going, it keeps coming up. Wherever that tunnel comes up our people would go there and fast there. That's where you'll find pictographs, because you're communicating with those spirits, those serpents.

Baataadowinan oogaawii miigi'ang Bagijeganan

Mewinzha gii ikdo, iwi ikwe gi'aayaa iwedi. Gii-oshkiniigikwewi, gaye abinoojiinyensan dako-binaawoaso iwe tikinagan, a'a tikinagan, mii ima iwi abinoojiinyens ima inagoojin mitigoon.

Gekendan, apii ezhi giizhig jeta anokiiwi apane, mii ojaanimizi. Giigooked, gakina gegoo izhijige mii' oabinoojiinyensen aabid iwedi mii gii nowaabi, waabimad anokiinid.

Iwi tikinagan giji apiitendagod iwe. AAoii dako-binigowin ino tikinaganing gikinawaabadan be-kaadiziwin, gikinawaabadan na'itamowin, gikinawaabadan ge'izhi awi-ginaawaabin. Be-toosh gaye gi'dakobinigowin, gitaa ima gimamaanaan Aki ikido, gi'dakobinigo iwi bi-madizi'aatig. Inowaan izhi'owinan gaa ogoode ima tikinaagan gijiwaawendaagwad shke idash wenji gikinoo'amowind o'o abinoonjii gegoo-wan agoodegan iwi.

Aniin igo,, mii' o'o abinoojiyens gaa izhijged, giin owaabimad omaamaa'iman. Ezhi biindiged owiigiwaam gegoo naazikaa. Agwajiing gi'izhaa abinoonjiiyens mii'apan. Ayaawan ima giimooji'ayaa izhikawen iwedi nibi.

CHAPTER SEVEN

Consequences of not Giving Offerings

They say a long time ago, this woman was there. She was a young mom, and she had her baby in a tikinagan, a cradleboard, and she had that baby hanging in a tree.

You know, back in those days you had to work all the time, so she was busy. She was making her fish, she was doing all sorts of stuff and her baby would just sit there and watch her, watch her work.

The tikinagan is a very special thing. When you're tied into that tikinagan you learn patience, you learn discipline, you learn how to watch. But you're also tied, you're in Mother Earth they say, you're tied to that tree of life. Those charms they hang on that tikinagan are very sacred and they teach the child things when you hang things on there.

Anyway, that's what that baby was doing, watching mommy work. She went into her wigwam to get something. When she came out the baby was gone. There were mysterious footprints that led to the water.

Ezhi baabiibaagind,"NI'ABINOOJIIYENS?" NI'ABINOOJIIYENS"
Gikendan, maajaa babaa izhaad igiwe aanid aa'aag,
"Gegoo ogii maaji-inaan ni'abinoojiiyens! Gii waabima
ina ni'abinoojiiyens? Ayaawan iwi bimikawaad bakobiid!"
Ga'awii'aa mikawasii o'o abinoojiiyens.

Geg aapii, gakina danakiiwin nandone'an o'o abinoojiiyens.
Iwi gidimaagi abinoojiiyens, gegoo maajiinagoon bakobiid.
Ikido gi'ayaagan bimikawaanan iwedi. Mii' geget, igi aa'aag
wenaanimize gaye miinowaa naandoma igi mashkikii aa'aag
jibi nanda-ninisidotamowad aaniin izhiseg.

Gii niizhio-wiijikiwendiwag, ogi ayaan Jiisikaan manidookewin,
ginaabj debwe Bebamash ezhinikaazo, gawiin igo aawi'an.
Mii' iwe niizh owiijikiwendiwag moozhag wiindan inowaan
dibaajimowian mii' o'o bezhig Bebamash.

Ogii ayaan manidookewin ima Jisikaan, ga'bimideg
babagiwayaanegamig, jigekenda-mowad ge'izhiseg. Iwenesh
ga'izhiseg iwi aki gibakise biinji'ii o'o ginebek zaagigweni and
wiindemowan igi mashkikiiainini, "Aa'aag gawi-in ozhitoonsii
bagijigenan. Aa'aag gaa gawesa izhijigisii mi'idash iwi gegoo
biinji'nibi maaji-inagoon iwedi abinoojiiyens."

Oonh aanish, igi mashkikii aa'aag gaa nakomin-dowe, gaye
iwi gaa diba'amaagewad inowaan aya'aa, iwi ginebek gaa
ayaad biinji'ii. Iwi gine-bek ikido, "Eya', gaa azheminin o'o
abinoojiiyens. Mi'idash eta bizishkendamiing, jiitaawapane
ogizhitoom nibi bagijiganan."

Gii ikido, "O'o abinoojiiyens aayaa iwedi aa-samajiw. Ji
moona'an." Mi iwa gawiindamow-enda. Mii, igi mashkikii
aa'aag windamowad igi aa'aag, " Izhaag iwedi aasamadinaang,
iwi anbinoojiiyens ayaad anaamayi'ii ini ini-naabikoog. Jiitaw
gaa moona'an."

She screamed, "MY BABY! MY BABY!" You know, she started to go around to the other people, "Something took my baby! Did you see my baby? There's tracks going into the water!" Nobody could find that baby.

Finally, that whole village was trying to look for that baby. That poor baby, something took it into the water. She said there's footprints there. Of course, the people panicked and again they called the medicine people to try to understand what happened.

There were two brothers, and they had a shaking tent ceremony, and I believe Bebamash was his name, I can't be certain. But those two brothers keep coming up in stories and one of them was Bebamash.

They had a ceremony at a Jiiskaan, a shaking tent, to try to find out what happened. What happened was that the ground opened up inside and a snake stuck its head out and told that medicine man, "People are not making their offerings. People are not doing that so that something in the water took that baby."

So of course, the medicine people tried to negotiate, and they tried to give payments to that being, that snake that was in there. The snake said, "Yes, I can give the baby back. But you must remember, you have to always make your water offerings."

They said, "The baby is in the side of that hill. You have to dig it out." That's what they told them. So, the medicine people told the people, "Go to that mountain on the side there, that baby is underneath those rocks. You gotta dig it out."

Mii, iwi gaa izhijiged, gaye gaa moona'an gebe'giizhig, Amaanj
igo minik daso'giizhig mii gaa gwemoona'ani. Gegopii, igi
gii'moonan, igi gaa bindaw giji waanzh, o'o abinoojiiyens
I,a ayaa, wenge gimo izhiyaa. Gawiin gego izhiyaasii iwe
abinoojiiyens, o'o abinoojiiyens wenge wewene ganawenema.

Iwi mashkikii inini, gaa odaapined ono abinoojiiyens gaye
gaa maajii bagosenimod mii' gaye inowaan abinoojiiyens, mii
gaa izhigewened ono omaamaayan. Gi'ikido, "Gikendan, iwi
abinoojiiyens apiiji giji apiitendagozi abinoojiiyens."Geget, iwi
abinoojiiyens gizhigid wenge gete aa'aawi. Biijinag gii miinaad
iwi omaamaawan, iwi mash-kikii inini biinjigwashkonid gaa izhi
googiid iwi zaaga'igan, gaa izhi enaadaagaad gaa ayaag iwedi
izhigewen ayaa, mii gaan'wiikaa gi'waabimasii miinowaa.
Geget igo iwe debwejimowin iwedi geget igo gaa izhiseg. Gaa
omeshkwadoonaan obimaadiziwin ini abinoojiiyensan.

So, they did, they went there, and they dug all day, I don't know how many days they tried to dig. Finally, when they dug, they got into a cavern and sure enough, that baby was there, that baby was in mint condition. Nothing was wrong with that baby, that baby was well taken care of.

That medicine man, he grabbed that baby and he prayed with that baby, and he brought it back to the mom. He said, "You know, this baby is a very special baby." Of course, that baby grew to be very old. After he gave it to the mom, that medicine man jumped and dived into the lake, and he swam down to where that tunnel is, and they never saw him again. That's a true story that really happened. He traded his own life for that baby.

Naanaagadawendaman Iwi Bagijigan

Gikendam ina, gi'anishinaabekawin awi'aa, gi'anishinaabekawin aa'aag, ayaa giji-inaakonigewin ayamaagad oma aki. Gikendan, gizhewaadiziwin, bagijiganan, manaaji'idiwin, bizaanendamowin, mii ino aki bagosenjigad. Daa apii ani-bangidenamin inowaan, aaniin apii inendomowin gaawn ji'izhimegasii gemaa gaye igi giji-zoongizi'ad ima ayaad, mii wiijii aa'aag onji gagwaadagitoowag. Mii gawiin gego jigeg-wedwewin.

Gaa Anisiinaabeyan, gii'okaademin zaagizi gaye biinjisi iwedi akiisan igi misi-ginebekoog gaye binesiweg gaye memegawansiwag, gaye nibi-inaabekwewag, gaye awesiinsag Gekendan, bimaadiziwinan imo gawiin giinadawind eta, niibiyo manidoog ayaawag imo aki. Gaa di'izhinadiziwin imio ayaa'ing o'o nibi, o'o noopiming, gikendan, ngoding wendad waniikenindaw gi'ayaad gawiinawaa ima.

Gikendan iwi gida abinoojiin izhi awaad giki-noo'amaadiiwigamig gabe giizhig, gabe hay giizhig o'o ogikinoo'amaage, gikenda izhise gegoo gaa inendamowin. Aaniish gaa izhi gikendamowad gegoowan? Aaniish gaa geget igo giji-gikendaasowad?

CHAPTER EIGHT

Thoughts on Offerings

You know, as an Anishinaabek people, an Indigenous people, there is a great law that exists in this land. You know, generosity, offerings, respect, dignity, the land insists upon that. When we fall away from it, when we decide not to give back or to give to the great powers that are here, then our people will suffer for it. There is no question.

As Indigenous people, we weave in and out of the territories of Serpents and Thunderbirds and Little People, and mermaids, and animals. You know, our life here is not just about us, there's a lot of spirits on this land. When we live our lives on the water, in the forest, you know, sometimes it's easy to forget that they are there.

You know when our kids go to school all day, all damn day in a classroom, you know that does something to their mind. How are they going to know anything? How are they going to be truly educated?

Iwi aki bagidenjige a ishpendaagoziwin giji-gikendaasowin iwa gidinwewininaan. Iwi bagidenjige o'o ishpendaagoziwin giji-gikendaasowin wii-miinaa'iing gida abinooji-inghminanik. Aaniish gaa izhi gikendamowad gaa izhidowad bagijiganan? Aaniish gaa izhi gikendamowad o'o aki dibishkoo ishpi'oninj gishpin gawesa izhaasii ingoji?

Ndebwedam iwi nawaj igo bangii gaa beskaamin. Gikendan, daga azhiweshkan gaye ezhikidowin, "Shaa, giinaawind mii' ozaam wenge gezhiikaamin! Gegoon wanisin gaye gaa gegooon waniikemin."

Ozaam gaa wi'bagijiganan gaye aaniish gi-inawind onji doodaman iwi gakina gegoo ima aki giji appitendaagwaad noongom. Ozaam gakina gikendamin iwi aki ezhiwebizid iwe aki'wiiwegimawan ingawanokiid, dibishkoo wenge gikaadendaagod iwe gegoo! Gaa izhi-webakin akiigaang i'i geget.

Gii gaa manezimin giji-aa'aag o'o bi ningod-waasimidana biboon iwi bami'idod gaa giji nibyo anishinaabe gidendaasowin gaa onisito-dan iwi gaa ombigi'ind inake. Shke eta, o'o bi ningodwaasimidana baboon, gaa nan-dawendamin inaa giji-aa'aag gaa nitaa-anishinaabemowad gemaa anishininiimo gikid-owin?

Gi'nandawendamanan inaa ji gikendamowad ini gegoonwan, ini manidookewinen? Gi'nandawendamanan inaa igiwe gikendamow-ad iwi aki biinjayi'ii gaye zaagijayi'ing? Mi'i apii, gaa ayaamin iwi ji'gikaadendaagod da niiskabi o'o izhiwebakin aki. Gaa gi'andawendamanan giji aa'aag gaa wiikaa ji waabidan binding ogiki-noo'amaage, eta gagikendamowad iwe noopiming.

Our land offers the highest form of education in our language. It offers the highest form of education that we can give our kids. How are they going to know how to make offerings? How are they going to know that land like the back of their hand if they're not out there?

I believe that it's time that we just slow down a little bit. You know, bloody take a step back and say, "Holy crap, we're going at this way too fast! We're missing something and we're forgetting something."

Because our offerings and how we interact with everything on the land is critical right now. Because we all know the world is going through an ecological collapse, like this is serious stuff! Climate change is real.

We need to have Elders in sixty years that are absolutely engulfed in traditional knowledge and understand that and were raised that way. Just think, in sixty years, do we want Elders that speak Anishinaabemowin or speak the native language?

Do we want them to know about these things, about ceremonies? Do we want them to know this land inside and out? In that time, we're going to be in a serious climate mess. We're going to need elders that have never seen the inside of a classroom, that only knew that bush.

Aangodinong, da ayaa iw abinoojiinh gaa mi-ingoowizid gaye apiji manidoowi. Gikendan, ayaawag mashkikii aa'aag, ayaad Jiisikaan aa'aag, gaa ayaad apiitendagozi miingoowiziwad. Aan-iish gaa onji'izhinad igiwe iwi giki-noo'amaagweigamig? Izhiwizh igi'wedi noopim-ing, mii izhi ikidowad gaa ningodwaasimidana biboon, "Ninitaawi'igo ima aki.. Ninitaawi'igoog nidede gaye nimama ima noopiming.

Iwi ninaagadawendaman ishpendaagwad. Mii aapii inaadiziwi ima aki gaye gii miinawa gaa manidoowan, mi api ganawendaming iwi gaa wiijigaabawitaadiwi ji'mashkwaag iwi gaa'ayaaning. Aapii ayaasii o'o aki, gaa izhi-toonsiii bagijiganan, giinawind aa'ii mino'ode'sii, gizhaadiziwin aa'aag gegi izha-yaa'ing.

Mii inowaan eta nendomowinan. Banaaji'we Anishinaabe inaakonigewin jimiinid i'i dagishkaawind odyaash gaye goji azhaa. Mi iwe inkidowan. Ayaawan bagijigan miinawaa; iwe aki izhi bagosenjigad iwi gizhewaadiziwin. Daga izhinada gidabinoojiinminanik noopiming giyabi'igo, gaye gaa dagishkaamin iwi Anishinaabe inaakonigewin ima odyaash, mii inendaman iwi apji ishpendaagwad, ge.

Occasionally, there'll be a young child that is very gifted and very spiritual. You know, they're medicine people, they're shaking tent people, they have special gifts. Why would you ever take them to the school? Take them to the bush, so that in sixty years they can say, "I was raised on the land. I was raised by my father and my mother in the bush."

That I think is important. It's when we live on the land and when we reconnect, that's when we're able to keep that relationship strong that we have. When we're not on the land, we're not making our offerings, we're not being those good-hearted, generous people that we're supposed to be.

Those are only my thoughts. Damn Indian Act needs to get a kick in the ass and get out. That's my message. There's offering again; there's the land which insists upon generosity. Let's get our kids out in the bush a little bit more, and we'll kick the Indian Act in the ass, I think that's really important, too.

BAKEBII'IGAN ZHAANGASO

Misi-ginebekoog gaye Miigaadiwinan

Daso-biboon gashkidoon gii nimoozhaginan gagwedwewinan ino aanind miigaadiwinan, aanind iwi miigaadiwinan api gaa izhiseg ima ga'ayaan akiins, gaye giji wiikoshkaagon ozaam inowaan dibaajimowinan apane ayaa misi-ginebekoog mikoma. Wawiikaa gii dibaajimow i'i miigaadiwinan gaye niiweshiwewinan miji dibaajimowad iwe misi-ginebek.

Mii inendaman iwi apji ishpendaagwad ji'ankinwaadenim iwi mewizha aa'aag, iko iwe gimiigaadiwad, ogi'ayaan manitooke, ge. Gawiin eta iwi omitigwaabiig gaye onibikwakan.

Gikendan, mewizha ogi daa izhindan ini inake babaamiwidoon omitigwanbig gaye onibikwak-an gaye ini bagamaaganan, mii izhidoowad igi-we binji'manidookewin, dash mooshkina iwi mashkikii jibwaa izhaad gamiigaading.

Menange, gii ikido igi neshenim giji zoongi'wag, gaye ima we akiins giiwataa gijigamiing gi'izhinikaananwa igiwe neshenim o'o Naadawek gaye mayaganishinaabe mii' moozhag gii mii miigaadamin mii' aabiding gwayakwaajimowing.

Gi'ikidog igi giji zoonigeziwad – igi Naadawek, ogashkitoon nawaad jii angonaagozi, gaye gaa noongaagosii, gii naangizide. Geget, ogi ayaan giji mashkiki gaye apiji gi'zanagad zhaa-gooji'iwenda – gii zanangozi ji nisaa ozaam ogi ayaan apiitendagoziwin mamaandaawizinan.

78

CHAPTER NINE

Serpents and Battles

Over the years I was able to collect information on some of the battles, some of the wars that took place in my region, and it was very fascinating because the stories always had serpents attached to them. Rarely did they ever talk about battle and their victories without talking about the Serpent.

I think it's really important to note that a long time ago people, when they battled, they had their spiritual power, too. It wasn't just with the bow and arrow.

You know, a long time ago they talked about how they'd take their bow and arrows and their clubs, and they'd take them into ceremony, and they'd be filled with medicine before they went to war.

Of course, they said that the enemy were very powerful, and in our region around the Great Lakes we called our enemy the Naadawek and they were a tribe that we often battled with at one time in our history.

They say that they were very powerful—the enemy, they could turn invisible, and you couldn't hear them, they were light footed. Of course, they had great medicine and they were really hard to defeat—they were hard to kill because they had special powers.

Igi aa'aag ima danakiiwin, apii iwi miigaadiwin gi'inakamigak, apii gii ayaag zanagise gii izhiseg. Gii bimi'ayaa dibikak, gii onigamiiwad dibikak wedagoshinowad ande igo ezhaad ozaam gii naniizaa izhijigewad megwaa gi'giizhikg.

Aanish, apii gii miigaading gaa odaapinegasii ino opiniin megwaa megwaa giizhikag, gaa gaye bagida'waasii gii mizhishawabi ozaam wegonen Naadawek waabimigog.

Mii', igi aa'aag ima danakiiwin api gaa izhise gaamiigaading, inowaan iko gaa adoopo wanagek biinji zhingwaak. Gaa noojitoowad ozibanaakwad, mii' izhi begishkada'waad, gaye izhi bakwezhiganikeyad. Mii' igo, bangii iwi goopaji' gagwedwewinan.

Awi miigaadiwin iwedi gaa izhise mewezhaa. Iwi miigaadiwin gosha gii maadakamigad daso-biboon jibwaa api apii oshkininis gii'igoshimo.i Iwi gwiiwizens, ezhinikaanid Mtigmish. Gi ozh-ki'awi, gemaa eta midasso biboone. Ookomisan ogii igoshimogoon. Ookomisan ikido, "Jitaa gaa da'igoshimo omikaan wi'igoshimo, mii geizhi bi'gikendaasowin.

Menwizha, apii gii izhind oshki aa'aag ji igo-shimo, mii iwi ji ayaad gikendamowin ima biinji oshtigwaan'an, biinjinaw. Mii' iwe gaa gikinaamaadi agamig. Aaniish, mii apii ezhi giizhigik gii debwetam iwi manidooke gikendaasowin. Mii iwa gaa giji apiitandagowad, gotaamigwendiz gaa ayaa– jii nisidotang gaa onagimigowin, gii manitoom ayaa ima aki.

Mii', apii gii inendagwod igi jii oshki a'aag wedi jii igoshomod, mii jii nitaawiginad ji'gwayakoshkaad, mii jii nitaawiginad iwi nib-waakaawinan i'I giiwitaa-aya'ii.

The people in my village, when this battle was going on, when the struggles were going on, they would travel at nighttime, they would portage at night to get where they were going to go because it was too risky to do that during the day.

Of course, during times of war you can't just go pick your potatoes during the day, you can't go set your nets out in the open because the enemy might see you.

So, the people in my village during times of war, they'd eat the bark off the inside of a white pine tree. They'd get that inner bark, and they'd pound it to a pulp, and they'd make bread out of it. But anyway, just a little bit of nerdy information.

This is a battle that took place a long time ago. The battle actually started many years before during a young boy's vision quest. There was a little boy, his name was Mtigmish. He was just young, maybe only ten years old. His grandmother put him out to fast. His grandmother said, "You must go fast to find your vision, so that you can be educated."

Long ago, when they put young people on the fast, that was so that they could get knowledge in their head, in their bodies. That was their school. Of course, back in those days they believed in spiritual education. That was the utmost, highest form of education there was—was to understand your role, your spirit in this land.

So, it was very critical to get the young people out there to fast, so that they could grow up right, so that they could grow up with good sense in their surroundings.

Iwi gwiiwizens, Mtigmish, mi'eta goji'igo midasso gemaa ashi-bezhig bibooniwi. Ook-omisan gi'izha iwi ayaa, gaye gaa izhi wende Chigidigan. Mi'iwedi izhinind gii ayaa giji mizhishinawabi gitigaan iwedi, gii ayaa giji-gitigaanan iwedi mewizha.

Gii izhinaa iwedi gaye gii ayaa giji wajiw iwedi gaye ookomisan izhinad ji'igoshimo iwi wajiw. Gii ikido "Mii' ima danaadiziwin baamaa ayaan bawaajigan."

Niso-giizhik jijise, nio-giizhik jijise, nano-giishik jijise-gawiin bawaajigan. Geg-apii gaa wi-indendamowa, "Gishpin ayaasii gii bawaajigan, mii' aaniish gi'izhigewin iwi gii bimaadiziwin? Gawiin gego ayaawaan gi'bimaadiziwin. Jitaa gaa mashkawizii, gaye jitaa gaa bagosenjige eni-gok iwi gi'bawaajigan."

Midaaso-giizhik iwe gwiiwizens gii igoshimod – midasso-giizhik mii' eta waaboowaan, mii' ogi ayaan obawaajigan. Ookomisan gegwejimogon, "Igi ayaan inaa iwi gi'bawaajigan?"

"Enyan, Gii ayaan! Giiayaan! Giin jitaa debwetan ggi ayaan!"

Gii ikido, "Wi gekendaman gishpin iwe bawaajigan ji debwewi, Jitaa ji ozhitoon ishkode. Da'ago bezhik eta zaka'an biiwaanag, o'o ininaabik. Gishpin ozhitoowan iwi ishkode aabiding zisikinebidoon, mii' gii gikendan gi'bawaajigan gii debweg gaye ji'bagidinaan ji ishkwa goshimon."

Mi'idash, ezhijiged naazikang ozibanaakwad iwi giizhikaatig gaye maaji ozhitood wadiswanens ini biisaa biiminakwaanensan ayaagan biinji wanagek, wenge agaasaabiigad – dibishkoo wi'nizisiman, gaye wadiswanens gaa izhi dakonaag ima oninjiin gaye ezhi bakitega' i'i. Bezhig zisikinebide ishpise gaye izhi biimiso niisaa-gizhibaabide gaye booniibide ima wadiswan, gaa maaji ish-kodewan.

This little boy, Mtigmish, he was only about ten or eleven years old. His grandmother went to this place, and they called it Chigidigan. They took him there and there was a big open field there, they had big gardens there a long time ago.

They took him there and there was a big mountain there, and his grandmother put him to fast on that mountain. She said, "You have to stay out here until you get your vision."

Three days pass, four days pass, five days pass—no vision. She finally told him, "If you don't have your vision, then what are you going to do with your life? You're not going to have anything in your life. You have to be strong, and you have to pray harder for your vision."

Ten days that boy fasted—ten days with only a blanket, and he got his vision. His grandmother asked him, "Did you get your vision?"

"Yeah, I got it! I got it! You better believe I got it!"

She says, "To know if this vision is true, I have to make a fire. With one strike of a flint, of a stone. If I can make this fire with one spark, then I know your vision is true and I'll release you from your fast."

So, what she did was she got the inner bark of a cedar tree and she started to make a little nest with those little strings that are in that bark, it's very fine—it's like hair, and she made a little nest and she held that in her hand and she hit it. One spark came up and it came spiraling down and it landed right in that nest, and it started on fire.

Ogikendan iwi Mtigmish, iwe obawaajigan gii debwe. Gaa
izhi gagwejimad, "Wegonen idash i'i?" ikidod, "Ni gi'ayaan i'i
bawaajigan gaa gi'ayaa zaagiiwan gaye iwi misi-ginebek agwaataa gaa izhi niigaanii nagonan biinji aa'ii gaamiigaadiwin,
gaa izhi niiwana'an. Mi iwa ni-bawaajigan." Iwi mindimooyeng
gikendam, AA HAAW. Ji maaji wezhi'aad o'o oshki aa'aa ji maaji
ojijiitaawi.

Gaye mii' gaa izhijige, izhi netaagig'a ji'gikendan wii izhaa
iwi miigaadiwin igoding gaye daa niigaanii igi aa'aag gaa
miigaadiwin ishkweyaang o'o misi-ginebek. Gii ombigi'in,
ogikendan gaa bekaadiziwin, ogikendan bizaa-naakwaa,
gikendamow ji'bizaanabi geaaya'ii, gikendamow awesiinyag
inwed, bineshiing in-we ji'gaganoonidiwaadmegwaa
gikinoontawaad apii miigaadiwin.

Gii gikinoo'amaawa o'o abinoojiinh jii babaa biijimaanjiged
wenge igo waasa, gaye debitam dibishkoo iwe awesii. Iwe
gwiiwezens wenge miinigoowizi. Mii', iwi oshki bimaadiz-iwin
mii' inake gaa nitaawigi. Gikenda, aapii gii oshkininiwi, apii
miigaadiwin gii ishise, gawiin gete awi'isii ikidowad.

Naazh iwi bakenaan endazhi', bakenad enda-zhiwad,
Missisaagiin izhi wende, niizho-wiijikiwendiwad gii
ayaa. Bezhig gaa wiijikiwen, wiinzo Baabaamaash, gaye
owiijikiwenyan gaa moozwe iwedi gaye gaa izhi ayaad omisad
dewizi. Wiin dash dibishkoo, "Onh nimisad nwiisagendam!"

Baabaamaash ikido, "Wengonesh gi'misad onji
wiisagendaman?"

"Amanj isa gema gaa miji'aan gegoon baa-naadad."
Owiijikiwenyan ikido, "Bagidinishin nininj atoonwan giimisad."

She knew that Mtigmish, that his vision, was true. And then she asked him, "What was it?" He said, "I had a dream that I was at the mouth of the river and a Serpent came out and it led us into battle, and we were victorious. That was my vision." The old lady knew, OK. We have to start preparing this young person to become a warrior.

And so that's what they did, they raised him knowing that he was going to go into battle one day and lead the people into battle behind a Serpent. As he was growing up, he learned how to be patient, he learned how to be still, he learned how to be silent for a long time, he learned how to do his animal calls, his bird calls so that they could talk code during times of war.

They trained that child to smell a long way away, to be able to see a long distance and to hear like an animal. That boy was very gifted. So, throughout his young life that's how they raised him. You know, when he was a young man, when the war took place, he wasn't that old they say.

Down in another place, another location, Missisaagiin is the name of that place, there were two brothers. One brother, his name was Baabaamaash, and his brother were hunting moose over there and his brother got a stomach ache. He's like, "Oh my stomach hurts!"

Baabaamaash said, "Why does your stomach hurt?"

"I don't know but I must've ate something bad." His brother said, "Let me put my hand on your stomach."

Ezhi atood oninj ima omisad gaye gegoo mikoojiin baamaajiseg biinji'omisad. Baabaa-maash ikido, "Jitaa gaa andawendan jii'ayaang manidookewin." Gaa maaji izhidetoowad ba-bagiwayaanegamigonens, aa'ii wiigiwamens, gaa izhi ayaad miidootsiinens biindig, gaa ma-doodoowens.

Ima madoodiswan owiijikiwenyan gii akozi gaye maaji zhishigagowaa ima mishoomis-inaabkinanag. Biinish gii zhishigagowan gegoo ima mamajise ini zhishigagowaan – mii' ingwa-na ginebekoons iwi, goji igo nizho'ininj ignigini.

Iwe ginebek bebamoode ima mishoomis-inaabkinanag gii biibaagi, mii gii nibo. Baabaa-maash ogikendan iwi Naadawek bi'ayaad. Igi Naadawek gawiin ganege waasa ayaad. Iwi ginebek gii wiindemaage.

Baabaamaash maajiinaad owiijikiwenyan, gii izhawag edndashi' ezhi wende Beshibii'igan Biisiboozh, mii' noongom wendeg. Mewizha iwe endazhi' mii' wende Kwekwezhoo'oong, iwe nibi gaa gwekwekibimijiwon, gwekweki, Kwekwezhoo'ong.

Mii iwedi gaa izhi'aad gaye gaa dibaajimowad igi aa'aag (ayaa mino aawangaa iwedi), "Gi-inawind jitaa goji ji'izhawin ima! Igi Naadawek, ayaawaa iwe Nskmok, ayaad neyaashi iwedi gaye wiimawine'ige.

Baaaamash wiindamowad iwi aa'aag, Mtigmish ayaa iwedi, gaye Mtigmish ikido, "Jitaa ji'biminizha'miing iw bawaajigan. Gaa azhegi-wemin iwi zaagiiwan, iwe misi-ginebek daa nii-gaanii biinji gaamiigaadiwin.

Mi'idash, gaa izhaad iwedi miigaadiwinwewig-amig iwe wii'nandobaniwad. Iwe miigaadiwin-wewigamig iwi giji-ininaabik. Iwi giji-ininaabik, ima agaamaai'ii ezhi wende Moozojaanhsing, Mooz ojaan.

He put his hand on his stomach and he could feel something move inside his stomach. Baabaamaash said, "We need to have a ceremony." They set up a little tent, a little hut, and they had a little midootsiinh in there, they had a little sweat.

In that sweat his brother got sick and started to throw up on those rocks. When he threw up something was wiggling in that vomit—it was a little snake, about the size of two fingers.

As that snake was crawling around in those rocks it screamed, and it died. Baabaamaash knew that the enemy was coming. The enemy wasn't even that far away. That snake warned them.

Baabaamaash took his brother, and they went to a place called Spanish Mills, they call it now. Long time ago that place was called Kwekwezhoo'ong, where the water goes back and forth, back and forth, Kwekwezhoo'ong.

That's where they went and they told the people there (there's a nice beach there), "We have to get out of here! The enemy, they're at Nskmok Neyaashiing, they're at the point up there and they're going to attack!"

Baabaamaash told the people, Mtigmish was there, and Mtigmish said, "We have to follow the dream. We have to go back to the mouth of the river, that Serpent will lead us into battle.

So, they went to the battle station where they're gonna launch war. That battle station was a big rock. That big rock, it's just on the other side of a place called Moozojaanhsing, Moose Nose.

Mtigmish gii ayaa iwedi gaye ozhitoon bagi-jiganan ino misi-ginebek, ozaam ayaa iwi misi-ginebek gaa bagone ima zaagiiwan, ayaa iwi izhiigewenan niisaabishka. Mii', izhaad iwedi, gaye ozhitoon obagijiganan gaye babi'o ino misi-ginebek jii mooshkiid.

Gezika, iwi nibi maaji biizitaaga, gaa maaji ditibiseg, minowaa gezika, makade ginebek, giji ginebek agwaataa. Iwi mis-ginebek maaji inaadagaa inagakeyaa Kwekwezhoo'ong. Mtig-mish ikido, "Daagaa maajaataa!" mii izhi nii-gaanii igi aa'aag ishkweyaang o'o misi-ginebek.

Megwaa gi'bimi'ayaad zhiibaatigoon, waabi-maad igi Naadawek imwedi agamayi'ii. Iwi Naadawek, wenge niibiyo, niibiyo gaye niibiyo igiwe. Igi baakaan odabwi gaa dibishkoo Anishinaabek, gaa odabwe dibishkoo Ojibweg.

Megwa gii odabwi'aad o'jiimaanan, baakaan izhiwe'idoon. Nisidawinaagwad ezhi gondaabi-igi'aad wiinawaa dabwi gawiin igi Ojibweg. Boozhke iwi aapijaag gikendagwad gawiin igi Ojibweg; igiwe Naadawek.

Mii, iwi gaa izhigiwad agwaabidoon wi'jimaanan iwedi zhiibaatigoon ayaag, gaa azhaad ishpiming gaa giimooji babaa'izha ishkweyaang. Megwaa iwe Naadawek gii zhiibaa'am, maaji apagi-jigewad asiniing igiwedi gaye ozhimaagani gaye nibikwakan.

Igi ininaabikoog dizhi bakite'o igiwe, gii daangiiwaabmag igi misi-ginebekoog gaa agwa-taad i'i nibi, naniibiyo! Gaa mawine'ige igi Naadawek. Iwi nibi onde, dizhi onde, aa'aazhawibide, onde, babaa mamaajii'aag, biimaskonewan. Iwi nibi, gwekweki'biijise! Gaa baawitgsinoon, mii miji'ayaag inake. Igi Naadawek gi'zhaagooji'aa ima.

Mtigmish was there and he made his offerings to the Serpent, because there's a serpent hole in the mouth of that river, there's a tunnel that goes down. So, he went there, and he made his offerings and he waited for that serpent to come up.

Suddenly, the water started to bubble, and it started to turn, and all of a sudden, a black snake, a big snake came out. The Serpent started to swim towards Kwekwezhoo'ong. Mtigmish said, "Let's go!" and led the people behind that Serpent.

As they're going through that channel, they could see the enemy on the other side. The enemy, there were lots of them, lots and lots of them. They didn't paddle like the Anishinaabek, they didn't paddle like Ojibwe.

When they paddled their canoes, they had a different style. You could tell by the way they dip their paddles in that they were not Ojibwe. Even from a distance you knew they were not Ojibwe; they were the enemy.

So, what they did was they parked their canoes where that channel is, and they got up on top and they snuck around back. As the enemy came through, they started to throw their rocks at them and their spears and their arrows.

As those rocks were hitting them, you should've seen the serpents that came out of the water, lots of them! They also attacked the enemy. The water was boiling, it was going back and forth, boiling, shifting around, twisting. That water, it was just flipping sideways! It had no current, it was just like this. The enemy was defeated there.

Bezhig gaa ayaa zhaabwii gii izkona, wiinjigazo Zhaashaa'animikiikaa. Iidig, ikido, "Gego nishi-kan! Gego mashi nishikan, nandawendam gii ganoonin! Zhaashaa'animikiikaa ikido, "Ngi'waabidan iwe aanakwad, iwe aanakwad gaa izhise o'o inini gaa gaa bi'niisaayi'aa gii waabimig bihiinaago dibikad gii wiindamaw gego aabijiitaa.

"Ozaam igi oshki-ogijiidaag gii inanaandam izhaad, daa ngagwe-gibijiii'aag. Nigiwaabidan iwi nibowin. Gaa wiikwajii'iwi gii zhaagoji' shke igiwe niojiidaamag gagiibaajichigewag gaye zha-zhiibitamoog." Gii ikido, "Mii' azha giitaa nizhiw. Giishka'an ninikan. Giitaa bigishkiw gaye giitaa na'inish igiwe nihi'aag.

Gii ikido, 'Gawiin gii odaapingosii, gawiin gaa ginodan nisigosi, giminwenimigo gosha noongom! Gawiin ginisigosi, azhegiiwen igiwe giji'aag."

Ezhi ikdo, "Gawiin. Mii' ima gaa ayaan igi niji a'aag. Gishpin nisigosi'an mi niin gaa nizidiz, niin giishka'an ninikan.: Mi iwe gaa ikidod.

Mii' waayagi'aad, Zhaashaa'animikiikaa gii nisa, miisa ogii manaadendamowaan ini. Betoosh gaa waabadibikad miinowaa bi ayaamagad endo-bandi'aad bi'aayaad gawiin awii'aa gikenjigesii. Zhaashaa'animikiikaa aazhaa gii nibo gaye ajigaazo baagwadinaa, owiiyaw jiigay'ii Asinish-waasining, o'o baakaan iwedi. Gawiin jimaami-nonendan igi Naadawek gii bi'aayaad miinowaa.

Gii ayaa iwi oshki-ogijiitaa, owiinzowin Mii'awas, mii iwe izhinikaanzod. Gi'ikido,"Gaa nandowaatoo'ad wiindamawgoog miinowaa endobandi'aad bi'aayaad, mii ayaawan denandam."

There was a survivor left, his name was Blue Thunder. Apparently, he said, "Don't kill me! Don't kill me yet, I need to speak to you!" Blue Thunder said, "I seen a cloud, that cloud turned into a man and came down and seen me yesterday night and told me not to proceed.

"But the young warriors wanted to go, I tried to stop them. I foreseen this death. You deserve this victory for my warriors were foolish and they didn't listen." He said, "Now you can kill me. Cut my arms off. Chop me up and bury me with my people."

They said, "No we don't want to take you, we don't want to kill now, we like you now! We don't want to kill you, go back to your people."

He said, "No. I stay with my people. If you don't kill me then I'll kill my own self, I'll chop my own arms off." That's what he said.

So unfortunately, Blue Thunder was killed, although they respected him. But the next night there was another war party coming that they never knew. Blue Thunder had already died and was put into a cave, his body near Asiniswaasining, this other place. They didn't realize that the enemy was coming again.

There was a young warrior, his name was Mii'awas, that was his name. He said, "My scouts told me there's another war party coming, and I have an idea."

Mtigmish wiindamaw, "Bizaan igo minizha'an aaniin igo gaa inendaman, daa minose izan. ozaam igoshim mozhag, gii gikendaas. Gitaa gashkitoon. Gaa gashkitoon iwe, wegonen igo nadawendaman," Mtigmish ikido, "Gaa wii-jii'igoo."

Mii'awas ikido, "Jitaa ji'izhaang iwe Nskmok Neyaashiing, iwedi neyaashiing. Gaa waan-ikemin gaa bagoneyaa'gamin ima aki. Gaa ag-wanii'dismowin api igi Naadawek gaa zhaabo bimose dibikak, mii' gaa mookiitawgamin igi.

Mtigmish told him, "Go with it. Whatever your idea is, it'll work because you fasted all the time, you're knowledgeable, you're educated. You can do this, whatever you need," Mtigmish said, "We'll help."

Mii'awas said, "We have to go to Nskmok Neyaashiing, to the point. We have to dig these holes in the ground. We'll cover ourselves up and when the enemy comes walking through at night, we'll ambush them."

Mii iwe gaa izhijige'ad, gii ozhiitaa'mowa ono bagoneygaann, binji niisaandawed ima magwa igi eko-nizhing endobandi'aad bi'aayaad gaye Mii'awas, gizaagiji-gwaashkoni iwi bagoneyaa, mii giji baabiibaagid. Giinoonjigaazo gii baabi-igagid bimi'aki, mii apiji gizhiiwe o obiibaagiwin mookiitagad ini naadawek, Mtigmish gaa ima odaanaaming. Gaa mookiitaaage geget gaa zhaagooji'iwed ini Naakawek.

Gii niizho-zhaabwe, mii' gaa izhijiged okiish-kijaane aayaan gaye gaa okiishkitawage aayaan, gaye gaa izhi bookonikebenaad. Gaa izhi wi-indamodaw, "Ezhegiiweg gaa onjii'ig. Gishpin bi-azhaaga'in ima bi gaa gwan nisaa'ing niji aa'aag gaa nagishkan bezhigwan bagwana." Mii' maajinaazha' i'i jiimaan.

Biijinag gaa izhise iwe, gaa izhaa iwe Asiniswaas-ining, gaa izhaa iwedi ininaabik iwedi Mitigmish daa izhi igoshimo gaye bagosenjiged gaye ozhitood bagigiganan. Gaa mama-zhinibii'ige iwi miigaadiwin ima igwe ini-nabikoog. Wiindeg Mazinabii'iganan, mazi-nabii'iganan. Gii inaabagjitoon iwi gaa miskwag zhizhoobii'igan, gaa mamazhinibii'ige iwi mii-gaadiwin ima ininaabik iwedi.

So that's what they did, they prepared those holes, they climbed inside there as the second war party came and Mii'awas, he jumped out of that hole, and he screamed very loud. They heard his scream all across the land, that's how loud he screamed, and he charged the enemy, Mtigmish right behind him. They attacked and of course they defeated the enemy.

There were two survivors, so what they did was they cut their noses off, and they cut their ears off, and they busted their arms. They told them, "Go back to where you come from. If you come back here and try to kill our people you will meet the same fate." And they sent them back in a canoe.

After this took place, they went to a Asiniswaasining, they went there to that rock where Mtigmish fasted and prayed and made offerings. They painted the battle on those rocks. They call that Mazinabii'iganan, pictographs. They used the red paint, and they painted that battle on that rock there.

Anishinaabek Miigaadiwinan

Iwi anishaabe miigaadiwinan giji imaanenda-mowin aapii igi aa'aag. Geget, api gii'izhiseg iwe nibiyo nishkenindiwin gaye nibiyo mawinadaan. Aa'aag gawiin ji'ishkwaa mii-gaazowad. Iwi miigaadiwin gaa dibaajimowan, ginwenzh izhise miziwe nibyo akiins aanike bimaadiziwin. Digo gegaa gii ininaa-naakawek iwe mayaganshinaabe.

Minowaa bakaan api, igi naakawek ayaad ima minis, agaye ayaawad gaa'andobaanii. Iwi mash-kikiinini, ikido, "Daa mookiitaagemin, geget." Ikido, "Gishpin gaa mookiitaasii igwedi, igiwedi gaa nisigomin!" Aani'izhaa, "Gikendan gaa izhi-jige." Mi'ikidod, "Gaa nandomanan iwi misi-ginebek, mii' nandomind iwe misi-ginebek, gaa bi-mookii."

Mii' mookiid daa aanamo iwi bagidanaamod ima zaaga'igan, daa giji'izhi binawan iwe zaa-ga'igan. Naakawek gaa daa gikenjigesii. Daa gijwise iwedi minis ozaam iwe binawan. Mii gaa gimooji'izhaamin iwedi gaye gega ni-sanaan gakina. Iwe gaa izhijigeying naazikowa-naan binesiyens gwiishkoshi ima minising gaa wiindamaagonan ande aayaad, ogii biminizha' mii' nanoondaagoziid iwe binesiyens."

CHAPTER TEN

Indian Wars

The Indian Wars were very sad time for our people. Of course, when this happened there was a lot of resentment and there was a lot of revenge. People didn't want to stop fighting. The battle that I'm talking about, it spanned a long time at many locations for generations. We were almost natural enemies with this tribe.

Another time, the enemy were on this island, and they were on a war path. This medicine man, he said, "We should attack, really." He said, "If we don't attack them, they're gonna kill us!" He goes, "I know what to do." He says, "We're gonna call a serpent, and when we call that serpent, it will come up."

"As it comes up it'll breathe its breath on the lake, it'll cause a big fog on that lake. The enemy won't even know. They'll be stuck on that island because of that fog. And we'll sneak up there and we'll kill them. What we'll do is we'll get a little bird to chirp on that island and tell us where they are, that way we'll just follow the sound of that bird."

Mii'sago iwe gaa izhijige, nondomwad ini misi-ginebek, gii bi-mooshkamo, aanamo iwi bagida-naamod, gaa'izhi binawan. Gaa izhi maaji noon-gaadozid iwi agaashiya nibi binesiyens. Mii'dash, igi Anishinaabek, bi-aayaad iwe jiimaanan, gaye giimoozkaw gaagiweg iwedi minis mii'dash zhaagoohi'aad igwedi. Mii' iwe gaa izhiseg.

Anind inowaan dibaajimowinan aayaawan apiji gagwaanisagitaagwadoon. Iwi wenjida igo gaa'izhijigen inowaan miiyawan, ga beshibii'win inowaan gaa izhijige'ad owiiyaw-ish, wiikomaad ini misi-ginebek nagaaj—gji aapiji, aapiji aakwaadiwag. Megwaa gi'izhise miigaadiwin, maaminonendam gii aayawaan nibiyo gaa'izhijigen ino dibaajimowinan. Goding maaminonendam inowaan dimaajimowinan ayaan gikinootawaagan, bakaan goding maami-nonendam gawiin goshaa, nmaaminonendam idash ayawaan wenjidoo debwe'inan.

So that's what they did, they called that serpent, it came up, it breathed its breath, and it caused the fog. That bird started to chirp, a little tiny water bird. And so, the Anishinaabek, they came with their canoes, and they snuck up on that island and they defeated them. That's what happened.

Some of these stories are really gruesome. The details of what they did to the bodies, the symbolism that they did with their remains, how they feasted to the Serpent after—it's really, really gory. During times of war, I think there's a lot of symbolism in these stories. Sometimes I think these stories are code, other times I think they are not, I think they're absolutely correct.

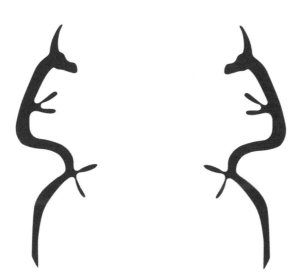

Gichi-Ashodamaagewinan

Daso-binboonagad, azhi gaa izhise, ino aanind enandam miigaadiwinan gaa izhise bimi', nii-zhonoon gikinawaabandiwin. Mii baamaa, azhi amanj minik wiikwajitoowad ayaawaad giji ashodamaagewin wiinowaa, geg apii gash-kitoowad.

Ezhinikaade Onaagan Wiiji'emikwaan, mii iwa ashodamaagewin zhego mayaganishinaabe awi gwayakonaagwad bekaadendan gabaya'ii dedi'izhse daso biboon. Genowenzh igo di'izhikewag, gaa dizhikewad dibishkoo, iwa minik agindaasowan, ganage ningodwaashwi maagizha niizhwaaso gagwe-gashkitoowad jii ayawad ashodamaagewin gaye ozhitoonaad be-kaadendam jibwaa aangwaamas.

Goding awii'aa wiijigaabawitaadiwad dago awii'aa gibayi'ii di'izhise jimino ganooniding iwe zhiingendawenjigenan, goding gaa gizh-kitoonsii aabiding wiikojitoosii. Mii' nayaanzh gaye nibiyo dasing wiikjitoo, apane wiikwa-jitoon, miinowa ji wiikwajitoon. Mii'iwe inen-damaan wenji ishpendaagwad ji nisidawendang apii gaa izhiseg gigaashipoose, nanda-gikendaming inowaan gii wanijige mii' gaa mi-inawa izhijigesii.

CHAPTER ELEVEN

Treaties

Years later, after these events took place, there's several battles took place by the way, these are only a couple of little examples. But afterwards, after how many times they tried to have treaty with each other, they finally got it right.

They call it A Dish with One Spoon, it's the treaty between the tribes that sanctioned a peace that would last for many years. Took them a while though, took them like, from what I can count, at least six or seven attempts of trying to have treaty and make peace before it was finalized.

Sometimes when you have a relationship with somebody it takes a long time to reconcile differences, sometimes you can't do it in one shot. It takes time and it takes many efforts, you gotta keep trying, and you gotta keep trying. But that's why I think it's important to understand what happened in the past, so we can learn from our mistakes and not do that again.

Gikendan, gi'ayaag iko miigaadiwin gaa gi'izhise, igi misi-ginebekoog gi'nandoma, aa'aag gii nibo. Gii'ayaa wasidaawendamowin, gii ayaa zhaa-goji'iam, gii ayaa jiikakamigad. Gegapii, gaa izhi maawanji'idiwad mii'dash giji-jiikendamoog oodemag! Mi'saa, nimaaminonendam inowaan gegoowan noongom.

Iwi jiibaygamigoon igwe naakawek gaa ning-wa'indwa, gikendan aande aanid inowaan giji-waawendaakaaeyaagan. Nimikwendam nigiizhi-gi'an aa'aag gi'ikidog iko, "Gagoo ishekan iwedi. Ozaam izhi'ayaan iwedi wiinawa omanidooya gemaa bi izhiweji'igoog. Gawwin iwedi izhaak-ag." Mii', Gawiin nikaa gii'izhise.

Nimikwendan gii'ishiseg Oaagan Wiiji'emikwaan manidookewiin gaa izhijegawad iko, aa'aag gii'izhaa inowaan jiibaygamigoon, gaa jiibenaake'ad igi jiibay gaye ashamaad. Mii'iwe mamakwendaman. Mii', nimaaminonendam iwe ishpendaagwad jii danaadizi iwe mino anokii iwe izhi-wiinde bekaadendan mi'igo ap-ane jiwiiji'zoongiziwin gaye maamawi'ayaad.

Odaa ayaan dibaajimowinan iwe apii gaa dangishkaagewin ini gii jiidiishiyan, gaye! Mi'igo iwe nidibaajimowinan ayaawan baabaasaabiki-zigedawan, ozaam gii Ojiwewiyan mi'idash inowaan dibaagjimowinan gaa gekendaman. Geget babaawaawiidamaageyan giin, wenge giikaamigomin

Dibishkoo ini gikinawaabandiwin iwedi Wa-zhask-Onigamiing gii niniiwenaagonan iwedi Wazhask-Onigamiing. Mii'sa, dibaajimowinan eyiizh ishisese, aa'ii eta iwe Anishinaabek azhedibaajim gaa'izhiseg inowaan aanind mii-gaadiwinan.

You know, there was a battle that took place, the serpents were called, people died. There was sorrow, there was victory, there were celebrations. In the end, we all ended up getting together and now we're one big happy family! So, I think about those things now.

The burial sites where the enemy are buried, I know where some of those sites are. I remember growing up people would say, "Don't go there. Because if you go there, their spirits might go back with you. You're not allowed to go there." So, I never really did.

I remember during A Dish with One Spoon ceremonies that they used to have, people would go to these burial sites, and they would feast those spirits and nourish them. That's what I remember. So, I think that it's important to continue that good work in the name of peace so that we can always be strong together and be unified.

They have their stories of when they kicked our ass, too! So even though my stories are biased, it's because I'm Ojibwe so it's the stories that I learned. But I guarantee you, we got a lickin'.

Like for example at Muskrat Portage, we got beat up at Muskrat Portage. So, the stories are both ways, this is only the Anishinaabek version of what happened in some of the battles.

Gegoo giiwiindemoon maamiikwendagod, gii ayaa iwi
mindimooyenh oma ishkonigan besho gaa ayaang gaye
odazhindan aaniish iwe aki-wenzii ayaa odaa wiigiwaam,
namadabi iwedi. Iwe akiwenzii gii mamaangitawage, noowaaj
igo niizhwaaitawagen inigokwaanegin, mii'on ezhi nitaawigi –
mii' gaa jii mingoowizi inake. Mii' eshtaa giji mamaangitawage

Mii'aaniinigo, wenge gii maangitawage ozaam noodawa' igi
naakawek. Gii'minjimendam dibishkoo gaa ezhi dibaajimonan
aazhigo, iwi naakawek gashkitoon gaawiin waabami-naagozisii,
mii' gaye izhinaagozi'ad ino awesi-insag. Idash, giji mii'
ngoowiziinowaan ino gi-ji'maangitawage mii jinooondawad igi
ozaam gaa waabimasii.

Iwi akiwenzii nabadabi biindigamigong mii' gezikaa, otawag
mamajiini, ogikendan geggo ayaa agwajiing, gaye apiji igo
enigok bizindam. Odebibidoon aanind mashkiki biijinisidoon
otawagan. Mii iwe mashkiki biinde, gakina gego onoondan,
gaye noondam igi naakawek odeb-itawa' wewiig biijise'ad
zhaaboo asaakamigoon. Igi naakawek waawiyekizowag
owiigiwaam.

Geget, akiwenzii, baakiinan gibishkwaande'on ezhi ikidod,
"Nida akiwensii'ow Gii bizaan igo giidaa nishiw gishpin iwe
andawendaman mii'dash gawiin aapiji gego bimaadiziwin
daa ayaansi, gawwin aapiji gego iwe zhaagoji'iam, gikendan
ayaan ima; ginoondoon. Mii gego noonde miiniwe gishipin
odaapinimon/" Mi'iwe gaa izhijegad odebibinaad ino
gimishoomisnan dewe'igan mii' izhi'asaad ima niigaan
gibishkwaande'on. Ezhi'ikidod, Ni an-dawwendan gakina
bizhiba-namadabi'ig oma bi ganawaabin.

I'm going to tell you something interesting, there was an old lady on the reserve next to us and she talked about how there was an old man in his wigwam, he was sitting there. The old man had real big ears, they were twice the size of a normal ear, he was born that way—he was gifted like that. Just a real frickin big ear.

But anyway, he had big ears because he can hear the enemy. Remember like what I was telling you before, the enemy can turn invisible, they had special powers, they can even turn into animals. So, he was gifted with those big ears so that he could hear them because you couldn't see them.

That old man was sitting in his lodge and all of a sudden, his ear started to twitch, he knew that something was outside, and he really listened hard. He grabbed some medicine and he shoved it in his ear. Once that medicine was there, he could hear everything, and he heard the pitter-patter of the enemy's feet walking quickly through the moss. The enemy had surrounded his lodge.

Of course, the old man, he opened his lodge door and he said, "I'm an old man. You can kill me if you want but there's not much life to me left, it's not going to be much of a victory. I know you're here; I can hear you. But I want to give you something if you'll take it." What he did was he grabbed his water drum and he put it in front of his wigwam door. He said, "I want you to all come sit around here and watch me."

Hay', onoondawa' ino bimikawaanan, gaa nam-adabi'ad iwe bikwadinaa niigaanii gaa ayaad mii' nisaa gii inaabiwad ino gaye ganawaabi-mawad. Oyaawaan inowaan gimishoomisnan dewe'igan, ekidod, "Wenzh igo gaa ma-maakwendaman igiwe mayaganishinaabe mii-gaadiwag. Wenzh igo gaa mamaakwendaman ayaa nisidiwinan. Iwenesh naa?

Ikido, "Gawiin gi'ayabi. Gishpin misawendizisii wii nisi'aan maagizhaa miigaadiwin daa gibijise aazha." Wiiji inikweni iwe bagijigan gaa izhi ikido, "gii miiniwe iwe dewe'igan," gaa izhi maajii dakobinad iwo dewe'igan, Megwaa dakobinad ino, nanagamo nagamonan ezhi'ikidod, "Nibagidinigamon inowaan niiwin nagamonan. Mii'inowaan nibagidiniganaan.."

Hay, baamaa noondewad animose'ad gaa ani maaja'ad. Gaa odaapinamowad ini nagamonan; odaapinamowad iniwe niiwin nagamonan. Mii'iwa gaa azhigane-ayi'ii bezhig iwe gwaya-kondiwinan gaa ayaagan. Hay, mii inowaan nagamonan gaye inowaan manidookewin iwe bekaadendan ayaamagad. Mi'iwe gaa izhiseg.

Gigikendan iwe misi-ginebek ayaa aagon-weyendaagoziwin aadisookaan, ayaa nibin aa-disookaan. Iwi gashki'wiziwin ino misi-ginebek ayamaagad imo biinjinawiiman ozaam wiiyawn-an ayaa nibi onji izhese gii wiiyawnan. Iwi misi-ginebek wenge giji manidoowaadizi. Gaa izhi Anishinaabekaag wenge gino wiijigaaba-witaadiwin' iwe misi-ginebek. Mii' noongom gii ayaabi wenji bagijigemin gaye bigagwedwewi-nan mii' iwe misi-ginebeg gaa izhi wiidookaazod megwaa gijiwaawendaagwad apii igiwe aa'aag banaaji'idowad iwe aki.

Sure enough he could hear those footprints, they all sat on a hill in front of him and they all looked down at him and watched. He had that water drum, he said, "For as long as I remember our tribes were fighting. For as long as I remember there was bloodshed. For what?"

He said, "No more. If you don't want to kill me then maybe the fighting should stop now." With a gesture of an offering and said, "I give you this drum," and he started to tie the drum up. As he was tying it, he was singing songs and he said, "I gift you four songs. This is what I give you."

Of course, after that he could hear them walking away and they left. They took those songs; they took those four songs. That was part of one of the agreements that we had. Of course, it's through songs and it's through ceremony that the peace is maintained. That's what happened.

You know the serpent is an incredible spirit, it's a water spirit. The power of that Serpent exists in our own bodies because our bodies are made of water. The Serpent is like a very spiritual thing. In our Anishinaabe ways we had a long relationship with that Serpent. So today we still make our offerings and our petitions to that Serpent so that it can help us during this very sacred time of when the human beings are destroying the Earth.

Megwaa iwi onagizhiyaabinan miji'izhiseg gaye gakina
dibaginjigwewinan gaa ayaa'iing iwe on-daadiziwinan
zhigwaajigewin, ozhitoowang ini bigagwedwewinan igwedi
gakina aki manidoog bi-izhaad jibi'wii wiidookaasowad
jiganawendawmo'da igi giji aanikoobijigan. Nii wiikwazomi'aa
iwe, Nii wiikwasomidagoz iwe jii danaadizi ji'izhijigewin
jitaa iwe izhijigewin jinaanaagadawenimwa gaye inowaan
giji-waawendaagakan bagijigenan iwegedi aya'aag. Mii'
inanademan giji ishpendaagwad.

Megwaa nagamowtowi iwe nibi, daa izhi nanagamowin
igwe nibi manidoog, ino naga-mowinan izhisewan ima nibi,
gii bagijigenan gaye izhisewan iwedi, gaa bagosenimowi
izhisewan iwedi gaye. Ayaawan inm nibi, min-jiminang iwe
minjimendamowin gaa gii izhese.

Gji aanikoobijiganani, megwaa minikweyaan iwe nibi,
ominikweyaan ino nagamowinan, ominikweyaan ino
bagosenimonan. Mii'sa mini-kweyaad inowaan bagijigenan
gaye ashima omanidoomya' gaye owiiyawan. Mii'dash,
megwaa ozhitoonwin inowaan bagijigenan, igi-we manidoog
daa ogii ganaanamawa' gii daa abinoojiminaanig megwaa
ayaad ima nibikaang. Mii' inake gaa izhi nitaawigi'ang, mii'
inake gaa izhi gikendamang.

Mii', izhi ishpendaagwad jii danaadizi izhi-jigewin ozaam
megwaa azhegiiwesii inowaan gegoo ayaa onjinewinan
gaye ini onjinewinan gaa zanaginaagwad. Mii' eta iwa
bigwajaya'ii inaakonigewinan. Gawiin niin ndozhitoozinan ino
inaakoniganiwinan! Mii'dash igo, mii' iwa bi'ekidowan.

Mii' eta gikinawaabandiwinan, nenibowa ayaawaan
babibaakaan gikinoo'amaagoowinan gaye
gikinawaabandiwinan, gaye inenimowinan, gaye
doodamowinan o'o misi-ginebek. Mii', bangii eta gaa
dookshkan gaagigidowin gaa mikwendaman.

During the pipeline struggles and all the problems that we're having with resource extraction, we've been making our petitions to all the spirits of the land to come and help protect our future generations. I encourage that, I encourage that we continue to commemorate and to make our sacred offerings to these beings. I think it's really important.

When we sing to that water, when we sing to those water spirits, our songs go into that water, our offerings go in there, our prayers go in there too. They exist in there in that water, it holds that memory of what happened.

Future generations, when they drink that water, they're drinking those songs, they're drinking those prayers. They're drinking those offerings and it nourishes their spirit and their bodies. Of course, when we make those offerings, those spirits will protect our children when they're around those waters. That's how we were raised, that's how we knew.

So, it's important to continue to do that because when we turn our back on those things there's consequences and the consequences are severe. It's just a natural law, I don't make the rules! But anyway, that's my message.

These are just examples, there's many different teachings, and examples, and ideas, and philosophies about the Serpent. So, I can only touch on a little bit of just a speak of what I remember.

Neniibowa ayaawaan gikinoo'amaagoowinan mii nii wiikwazomag gakina awii'aa babaa-izhaayan ingoji, gaganoozh igi giji aa'aag, biidoon gakina gego inowaan biinji izhigiizhwewin e-gikinoo'amaagesaadagamig, jiikendaagwad gozha! Minjimendan inowaan bagijigenan gaye gegoon, gakina gegoo gash-kijigaade.

There's lots of teachings so I encourage all of you to get out there, speak to your elders, bring all these things into language class, it's fun! Remember that with our offerings and things, everything is possible.

BAKEBII'IGAN ASHI-NIIZH

Anangoowininiwag

Igiwe giji aa'aag apane gii ikido iwe-ayaad anangoowiningwag ima gii endaadiziwad azhaa, gaa ayaawag ima. Bakaaninaagoziwag, gaye wenge gaa nisidawinaagozi maadaawanidiwad. Niiwi daa wiindemago igwe Anangoowininiwag apane ayaawad ima. Gii ayaa azhigane-ayi'ii maada'okii ima aki. Iwe goding gii ayaawad o'o gijiwaawendaagwad wiigiwaam ima aki.

Getget, nibiyo' giinawind gii debwetamin iwe ondaadiziwin igi anangoog, boozhkaa giinawiind aa'aag anangoowininiwag gaye, mii' iwedi on-daadiziing. Nmikwendaman, gii wiindimon dibaajimowin gaa wiindamogowan iwa giji in-zhishenh gaa gii, shaa, booshke gegaa go ingodwaak biboone gii wiindemowid iwe dadi-baajimod.

Gii ayaa iwe Aki Miigaadiwin Bezhig gaye Aki Miigaadiwin Niizh ojijiitaa. Mii iwa dibaajimo-dowed, gaye gegaa gakina igiwe oodemag gii debwetam inowaan dibaagjimownan ozaam igiwe giji aa'aag gii kido wiinowaa giji aa'aamiyaa dibaajimowad.

Mii iwa gaa dibaajimodowid, "Gikendan, iwe ani akiiwang igiwe Anangoowininiwag daa bi-niisaawi'ad ima aki. Daa ayaa giji miigaadiwin mii' iwa gaa izhise. Aa'aag daa ani miigaadiwag iwe nibi. Mayaganishinaabg, aa'aag gaa noonde banaaji'ayaad igiwedi. Mii' gaa ogii gash-kitoonsii. Ozaam megwaa aapii azhaa gaa ozhi-toomin bagijigenan o'o giizhigo, gaye gaa wiikomaanan Anangoowininiwag daa bi niisaawiyad gaye gaa wiijii'igonaan jii ayaag i'i mino-miziwe-aki.

CHAPTER TWELVE

Star People

The old people always said that there's Star People that are living amongst us already, that they are here. That they look different, and you can pick them out in a crowd. I was told that the Star People have always been here. That they are part of the existence here on Earth. That sometimes they live in the sacred lodge here on Earth.

Of course, many of us believe that we come from the stars, that we ourselves are Star People too, and that is where we come from. I remember, I am going to tell you a story that I was told by my great uncle who was, jeez, he must have been almost 100 years old when he told me this story.

He was a World War I and a World War II veteran. This is what he told me, and a lot of the family believes these stories because those old people said that old people told them.

This is what he told me, "You know, in the future the Star People are going to come down to the Earth. There is going to be a big war that is going to happen. People are going to be fighting over water. The native people, people are gonna wanna destroy them. But they are not going to be able to. Because at that time we are going to be making offerings for the sky, and we're going to be inviting the Star People to come down and join us to make the world better."

Gii ikido iwe daa izhise iwe gaye jibwaa izhise, giinawind gaa waabidamin giji waazakone ima giizhigo, dibishkoo jiingwanan, mii' apii aki gaa aanjise. Gii ikido iko igiwe Anangoowininiwag daa bi wiisookewag. Daa bi wiisookaaged, gaa wiisookaaged igiwe, mii'dash bagosenimoda jibji wiisookaaged, daa bi'izhawag.

Ino giji bagamaaganan gaa aabajitoowad apii iwi miigaaziwad gaa gashkitoonsii gaa wanaan-imizisii gashki'wiziwin ayaad igi Anangoo-wininiwag. Iwi Anangoowininiwag, aapii bi niisaawiyad, gaa maajiinigonan aanind iwedi ishpayi'ii gaa ondaddiziwad, mii' iwa gaa inaajimotawgowan.

Gigenimag nibyo giji aa'aag noongom gaa ikido iwe maa onji giji aa'aawiyad ozaam baabii'dowad iwe ji'izhiseg. Iwe Anishinaabe inaadiziwin mii' iwa nibyo aa'aag debwe-tamowad igiwe Anangoowininiwag bi ayaad mii'dash gaa-niigani-dibaajimodjig, gaa-niigani-dibaajimodjig azha miwezha wii bi'izhaad gaye bi' wiisookaaged megwaa daa zanagad miigaa-diwin. Ndebwedam iwe ozaam wegonen igiwe giji aa'aad gaonji giiwanimowad

Gi anshinaabewiyan, zhigo giita ayaamin giji nibyo debwe'endaagoziwin igiwe Anangoo-wininiwag azhaa, dibishkoo azhaa gaagiji apiitendagozi manidoo izhi-wiinzo Niigaanini, aanii niigaanii giinawind ima aki mii'iwedi aan-ikeshkaw aki.

Mii' giitaawanan Nookomis, gaa giji apiitend-agozi aa'aa endinadizi iwe desa'giiin iwe miikaans iwide anangoog jibwaa ani izhaa iwe jiibay miikana.

Gaa daa ayaawanan gaye Jiibayaboos, ayaa giji Manidoowi aa'aa, Nenaboozhoo owiijikiwend-iway mii' ima inaadiziwad iwe Jiibay Miikana gaye wiidookaazo aa'aag iwide Jiibay aki mii'iwedi gaa izhaawi.

They said that this is going to happen and that before it happens, we are going to see a big light in the sky, like a comet, and that is when the world is going to change. They said that the Star People are going to help. They are going to help, they are helpers, and when we ask for their help, they are going to come.

The big weapons that are going to be used during this war will not be able to phase the power of these Star People. The Star People, when they come down, they are going to take some of us up back to where we come from, is what I was told.

I know a lot of Elders today that say that the reason they are growing so old is because they are waiting for this to happen. In Ojibwe culture that is what many people believe that the Star People are coming and that it was prophesied, that it was foretold long ago that they were going to come and help us during a tough time of war. I believe that because why would those old people lie?

As an Anishinaabe people, we already have so many allegiances with Star People already, like we have a very special spirit that we call Niigaanini, which leads us from this world out into the next world.

Then we have Nookomis, a very spiritual Star being that lives at the crutch of a path in the stars before we go to the Milky Way.

We also have Jiibayaboos, who is a very spiritual Being, Nenaboozhoo's brother that lives in the Milky Way and assists people to the spirit world where we go.

Apane gii ikido gii ayaagan nibiyo giibaakaangan akiin, jiibay akiin ingoji gaa gi bezhigwan. Apane ndebwetam bezhig gizhigik iwe mino-miziwe-aki ozaam mii iwa gaa wiindamagowan..

Mii igi awesiinsag gaa wiinowaa ozhitoonwa bigagwedwewinan igiwe Anangoowininiwag ozaam igi awesiinsag ayaawag gijiwaawen-daagwad debwe'endaagoziwin igiwe anangong. Gikendan, gii ginawaabimindwa iwe anangong mii' waabidaman iwe anangookag, gii waabima gakina igi awesiinsag gaa ishpayi'ii. Gii waangoomidiminoog mii' ezhi odode'ad.

Mii' igo, giinwaabimidwa ishpayi'ii igiwe anangoog ino ezhi gijiwaawendaakaa, igiwe awesiinsag. Gawiin wanijige, ginetaawin gaa anishinaabewin gaa'ozhidowad inowaan bigag-wedwewinan, shke igiwe awesiinsag gaye gaa ozhidowad gaye, mii' gakina gaa bimaadizi aa'aa ima aki mii' gaa ozhitoowad ini bigagwedwewi-nan mii'dash o'o aki ge ani mino miziwe.

Gikendan, nimaamaa, gii oshki maamaayan, gii'izhitaa iwe waakaa'igaans. Gezikaa, onoon-dan madwesin inwewe, iwe inwewe mamadwetoo gaa izhi maajii niningishkaa waakaa'igaans, maajii niningishkaa. Gii ani ze-gisi, inaabi agwajiing, gii dibikad. Digo dibish-koo bagakaaban iwedi agwajiing, Giji baagakaate igo eta aapiji waasakone miziwe. Agwajiing gii ayaa aapiji waasakone on-daaboodemagad ishpayi'ii waakaa'igaans.

Mii', gii biindigebatoo, gii agwani'ig, "Gego odaapinagag ni'abinoojiins! Gego odaapinagag ni'abinoojiins! Niiin odaapinashin dash gego odaapinagag ni'abinoojiins!" Gezika iwe gegoo miji maajiibide wewiib gaye angose inwedi noopiming.

They always said that there are many different worlds, spirit worlds out there and that they are not all the same. I always believed that one day this Earth will be better because that is what I was told.

That the animals will also make petitions to the Star People because the animals have a very sacred allegiance with the stars. You know, when you look up at the stars and you see the constellations, you see all those animals up there. They adopted each other and they are family.

So, when you look up at those stars, those are sacred sites, those animals. Make no mistake, it is not only us as Anishinaabe people that will be making those petitions, but the animals will be making them too, and all the living things on Earth are going to be making petitions so that this world could become a better place.

You know, my mother, when she was a young mom, she was living in this little shack. Suddenly, she could hear this humming noise, this noise came and started to shake the little shack, started to shake. She got scared, she looked outside, it was nighttime. It was just like daylight out there, great big floodlights that just completely lit up the whole area. Outside there was a great big light hovering above the shack.

So, she ran inside, and she covered me up, "Don't take my baby! Don't take my baby! Take me but don't take my baby!" All of a sudden that thing just shot off quickly and it disappeared into the forest.

Nidebwetan iwe gii izhise, gawiin jiibabaa-giiwanimod
iwe. Daa apane nitaagigo'yan iwe debwetamowin iwedi
gegoo gii ayaag ingoji, iwedi gegoo gii ayaag ingoji. Iwedi.
Gawiin mininaak ni gegoo jii ayaag ingoji iwedi; o'o gaagige-
giizhig wenge giji miijaa. Gaa'izhi inaadiziwinan, gaa'izhi
manidoowaadiziwin, gii debwetam iwe giizhig moozhkina o'o
manidookenan aa'ii gaa ayaa nibyo jiibay akiin ingoji iwedi
gaye mii' igo giji maamakaaden-daagwad sago gakina.

Gawiin wanijige, ingo-giizhik daa bi ayaawag ima. Nibyo
ayaawaan mazinibii'iganan, nibyo ditibinaaganan, nibyo gete
dibaajimowinan igi-we bi-niisaawi'ad gaye bi wiisookaagewin.
Mii', niin dakonan iwe. Nidebwetam igo noongom iwe, iwe giji
gijiwaawendaagwad aapi gii ayaang, giji gijiwaawendaagwad
aapi ozaam nii-zho'kaadaad nishwanaaji'igewag gakina gego.

Gitaayamin aa'ii giji doodamowin jii dakonami-in iwe
manidoowaadiziwin, jii dakonamiin gii dibaajimowinan,
jii dakonamiing inowaan giji gete nibwaakaawinan gii
nagadamaw, mii inowaan dibishkoo gashkibijiganan am
gikendaasowinan. Ino dibaajimonan mii iwe azhigane-
ayi'ii. Goding zanagad jii debwetang, noongam iwe aki,
igiwe Anangoowininiwag oma daa bi izhaa ima gaye
daa wiisookaagewag gaye wiisooked bimaaji gegoo. Gii
wiidibaajimigo aanind gii odaapinigomin mii' izhigewenigomin
iwe gaa wenjiiwi o'o anangoog. Gaa noonde wiindamon iwe.

Gii makawa ininaabik gaa gii ezhi abiyaan, gaye ima ininaabik,
ayaawaan mazinaakiziganan giizhigong-naabikwaanan
mikigaade ima ini-naabik, ingwana gete ininaabik. Ini
wiinawaa gaa doodamowad a'a Anishinaabemowin mazi-
nabi'igan, wiinowaa gaa doodamowad mazi-naazowinan a'a
wiiji aa'aag.

I believe that it happened, and she would not lie about that. I have always grown up with the belief that there is something else out there, there is something else out there. It is impossible for something not to be out there; the galaxy is so huge. In our ways, in our spirituality, we believe that the sky is filled with spirits and that there are many spirit worlds out there and it is a great mystery about it all.

Make no mistake, one day they will come here. There are lots of pictographs, lots of scrolls, lots of old stories about them coming down and helping us. So, I hold on to that. I believe that right now, this very sacred time that we are in, is a very sacred time because the two-legged are trying to destroy everything.

We have a huge responsibility to hold on to our spirituality, to hang on to our stories, to hang on to those very ancient wisdoms that were left to us, they are like bundles of knowledge. These stories are a part of that. Sometimes it is hard to believe, in today's world, that Star People are going to come here and help save everything. I was told that some of us will get picked up and brought back to where we come from in the stars. I just wanted to share that with you.

There was a rock found where I lived, and on that rock, there are pictures of spaceships that were found on that rock, the rock was old. It was done in Anishinaabemowin mazinabii'igan, was done through the drawings of our people.

Mii', giiyaabi debwetamoog. Gaa debwetwakan igi aa'aag, debwetan ino gakina gegoowan. Miz-iwe aki babekaan manidoo inenimowinan gaye babekaan debweyenan. Denandam iwe mamawi'ijigategin mii' daa miikawaadendaagod naabinigan daa aabiziishin. Apane gii piitenn-dam igwedi aa'aag inenimowinan gaye wiinowa inendamowinan gaye odaa dibaajimowinan.

Gikendan, gii wiindamagomin iwe noongm bimaadiziwin, ima aki, ayaa agwaniiwin iwe miikawaadendaagozi anang mashkiki. Iwe An-ishinaabe Aadisookaan, iwe oshkiniigikwe gi-gibangishin iwedi dibiki-giizis mii' boonii ino nibi ima. Aaptt giboonii ima nibi ogii ayaan mashkiki mashkimod, gaye iwe mashkiki mash-kimod giibakise, mii' gakina anang mashkiki biiwise miziwe nibi.

Ikido iwe mnidoonhs, ezhi'wiizowad Mnidoonhs, mndoonsag. Babaa ayaad, babaa maawanjitoonwad iwe anang mashkiki, mii ima ezhi atoowad opikwanang. Aanapii igi awesi-insag gii nibo, we mashkiki atoonwa opikwa-nang agonde agamiing mii' inowaan miigisag.

Igiwe miigisag ayaawag anang mashkiki.

Mii' gonasha giwiji aa'aag ogii aabaji'ayaad min-ik wenge gaye debwetanimaan minik wegen, ozaam ayaawag gijiwaawendaagwad. Igi miigisag odokanaan gakina aandaakonigeminaan gaye gakina gaa nisidotamiing, gakina onji apiitaami-kaag o'o nibi mii' iwedi ishpiming binji anangoog, gakina gii aandaakonigeminaan giki-nootawaagan ayaawaan binji miigisag.

So, keep believing. Just do not believe in people, believe in all sorts of things. All over the world there are different spiritual ideas and there are different beliefs. I think that when you put them all together, it makes a beautiful puzzle come to life. I always respect other people's ideas and their thoughts and their stories.

You know, we were told that this life, here on Earth, is covered with beautiful star medicine. In our creation story, a young lady fell from the moon and landed in the waters here. When she landed in the waters she had a medicine bag, and that medicine bag opened, and all her star medicines scattered all over the water.

They say that these little creatures, they call them Mnidoonhs, mnidoonsag. They go around, they collect that star medicine, they put it on their back. When those little animals die, that medicine on their back washes up onto the shore, those are the shells.

Those shells are star medicine.

That is why our people used them so much and believed in so much, because they are very sacred. Those shells hold all our laws and all our understandings, from the very depths of the water all the way up into the stars, all our laws are coded in those shells.

Nmikwenima gaa minonaagozi giji aa'aa, gii wi-indemag
abiding ookomisan miinigoon aanind miigisag, niizh eta igi,
gaa atoon binji omooday. Mii' ima naganad daso-biboon.
Gii azhagiwe odibaabamad ini, o'o omooday gegaa moozhkina' igi miigisag. Igwedi niizho-miigisag maajii ayaawaad
abinoojeiinyensag gii niizhiwad, mii'dash nibyo ayaawaad
abinoojiinyiwag mii'sa iwe omooday moozhkina' igiwe
miigisag.

Igiwe miigisag ayaawag gijiwaawendaanimaan niinawind.
Nidebwetam ayaawad minik manidooke, wenge nibyo
mink manidooke iwe bingi miigis. Mii', gegashkiw igiwe,
wawezhi'izo miiwan igiwe, wawezhi'itizowag miiwan ino
waawendaagamagin mii ishpagoode. Mii' iwa ezhijigeying api
piizikowaang igiwe gii'miigisan.

I remember this beautiful Elder, she told me that one time her grandmother gave her some shells, just a couple of them, and she put them in a jar. She left them there for years. She went back to go check up on them, and that jar was just almost filled with shells. Those two shells started to have babies with each other, and they had a whole bunch of children and that jar filled up with those shells.

Those shells are very sacred to us. I believe there is so much power, there is so much medicine in a shell. So, wear them, adorn yourself with them, decorate yourself with the sacred that hangs in the sky. That is what we do when we put our shells on.

Ndodaapinen iwe apiji gikaadendaagod, mii'iwe gegoo iwe gaa wenge giji debwetan ozaam mii'iwa getc aa'aag gaa ikido. Mii' gimiji wi-indamon iwe, gaye gi'yaabi gegoo jii debaajigadag igi anangoog gaye gakina. Api idash bezhigo-giizhig gaa gashkijigemon iwe.

Giitaa debwetaage, iwe aki onadawenima' gaa niitaa debwetaaged. Azhaa de-minik aa'aag ima aki gaa aagonwetamowad a'a gaa gegoo, mii'iidog gakina gegoo ombwewegbitoonaad. Gaye giitaa debweyaage iwe bagosedan iwe debweyendamowin, iwe gaye Anangoowinini-wag ozaam wiibi ayaawag.

Jiitaa igo giziibiigindiben gaye bizziwaabide'on, gikendan? Giziibiigiingwe'on gii gigizheb! Gishhpin ima bi'izhaad mii gaa waabimigo wi-ininiaagoziwin, gaa onizhishinsiinoon, gikendan? Bijikonayen gaa onizhishin gigish-kiganan, ganawenindizon.

I take this very seriously; this is something that I really believe because it is what the old people said. So, I just wanted to share that with you and that there is so much cool stuff to be told about the stars and all that. Hopefully one day we will be able to do that.

Be a believer, the world needs believers. We have enough people in this world that do not believe in anything, they just bugger everything up. Also be a believer of hope, of faith, and Star People because they are coming.

Make sure that you wash your hair and brush your teeth, you know? Wash your face in the morning! If they come here and they see you all grubby, that would not be too cool, you know? Put on some good clothes, take care of yourself!

Inaakonigewin

Wegonen iwe inaakonigewin? Wegonesh iwe enkidon? Mewinzha, igiwe gete aa'aag apane ikido gii ayaag gegoo ima aki, iwe minonaagwad waabooyaan a'a bimaadiziwin, gaye gakina iwe aki inaakoniggewin gaa-apikaadeg binji iwe getewaawendaagwad waabooyaan.

Gaa ezhi Anishinaabewin, api ima gaa bi izhaawin iwe aki gagiinawind apikaanigomin binji iwedi getewaawendaagwad waabooyaan a'a inaakonigewin. Mii' iwe ogimaakandan gakina gegoo.

Gakina awesiinsag ogikendanawan iwe inaaki-nogewin. Igiwe anangoog ogikendanawan iwe inaakinogewin, iwe aanakwadog... Gakina miit-igog gaye iwe gitigaadan ogikendanawan iwe inaakinogewin, boshka gaye gimiwan ogikendan iwe. Gakina gegoo a'a zagaabiiginon biinji i'i minonaagwad waabooyaan a'a bimaadiziwin. Wenge nibyo gaa onizhishin, gaye ayaawan giii nibyo mamaandaagojigenan biinji i'i mi-nonaagwad waabooyaan a'a bimaadiziwin gaa gimiinigoziwin.

Wii' biindegiwin iwe getewaawendaagwad wii-giwaam i'i bimaadiziwin ima aki, inowaan inaakonigewin miziwe gii babaa'ayaawan. Igi awesiinsag mi'igiwe gaa niigaaniiwad iwe gii'ogimaawiwinan. Mi'iwe gakina gegoo ima inaadiziwin gaa mikawaamigowin ino inaakonigewinan. Mi'iwa debwewi inaakonigewin, aanish mi'iwe gegoo ji bimin-ishowemiing gii anishinaabewin, gawiin iwe Anishinaabe inaakonigewin gawiin ino gaanada ogimaawiwin inaakonigewinan.

CHAPTER THIRTEEN

Law

What is law? What does that actually mean? Many years ago, the old people always said that there was something here on this Earth, this beautiful blanket of life, and all the Earth's laws were weaved into the sacred blanket.

As Anishinaabe people, when we come to this Earth we too get weaved into that sacred blanket of law. It is what governs everything.

All the animals know that law. The stars know that law, the clouds... All the trees and the plants know that law, even the rain knows it. Everything is connected into this beautiful blanket of life. There's so much beauty, and there's so much magic inside this beautiful blanket of life that we have been given.

As we enter the sacred lodge of life here on Earth, these laws are all around us. It is the animals that are the leaders of our government. It is everything in nature that reminds us of these laws. That is the true law, which is something that we must follow as Anishinaabe people, not the Indian Act, not the Canadian government's laws.

Nitaa mino izhijiigewin, gaa izhi nitaa ganawen-imidewi, gaa izhi nitaa mino-minwaabamewizlwin gii wijii aa'aag, gaa izhi nitaa minwaabamedan iwe aki- gakina iwe ayaag gaa gikinootawaad ima biinji i'i mi-nonaagwad waabooyaan a'a bimaadiziwin. Gakina gegoo ima ayaamagad.

Mii' gakina gaa zagakimgad gii odishiwe gaa bi'izhaad ima aki, wiizhaamanad iwe biinji i'i minonaagwad waabooyaan a'a binaadiziwin mi'igiwe gi- aanikoobijiganani jii ayaad gikendamowin iwe izhi onizhishin gaye giji ganawenimigoziwin ino inaakonigewinan.

Apii wii boonendaman ino inaakonigewinan, api gaa ginage biminizha'sii iwe inaakonigewi-nan, gaa ani majendaagozimin iwe inaapinewin gaye nibowin. Mii' ani gwenawi-doodamin i'i gakina gegoo iwe gawiin onji onizhishin. Iwe inaakonigewin ganawenimigonan, i'i ganawen-imigonan iwe inaapinewin, iwe bakadekamigad, iwe aakoziwin, iwe igo geyaabi.

Inowaan gakina gaa minonaagwagin gaa ayaagan ima biinji giji inaakonigewin i'i biinad mashkiki i'i wiji aa'aag. Gawiin aawii'aa ima aki ji agaanzomid jii andawendamiing iwe iwe An-ishinaabe inaakoginewin. Gawiin aawii'aa ima jii agaanzomid iwe giji inaakonigewin ima ayaag gaa noopimiing, aki, nibikang, gaye mashkoo-degoog, manidookewinan, gaye an-ishinaabemowin, gitaa jiigi naabishkawgad iwe-di Odaawa. Gawiin gegoo odashkitoonsiin jii agaanzomid iwe.

How to be good, how to take care of one another, how to treat people with respect, how to respect the Earth—all of that is coded in this beautiful blanket of life. Everything is there.

For all the settlers and newcomers that come here to these lands, we invite them into this beautiful blanket of life so that the next generations get to experience the beauty and the great protection of these laws.

When we ignore these laws, when we do not follow those laws, we become vulnerable to disease and death. We become vulnerable to all sorts of things that are not good. The law protects us, it protects us from disease, from famine, from sickness, from more.

All these beautiful things that exist in this great law is pure medicine for our people. There is nobody on this planet that can convince me that we need the Indian Act. There is nobody that can convince me the great law that exists in our forest, our lands, our waters, and our plains, our ceremonies, and our language, can be replaced by Ottawa. There is nothing that can convince me of that.

Mii', aa'aag bezaan wii'ikidowad iwe gaa ndan-wewetoowan…
Na shke giiwiin dibaajimodoon gaegoo, ishkwaa-giizhigad mii'
inowaan inaakonigewinan, mii jii ayaag ino mi-nonaagwad
waabooyaan a'a bimaadiziwin aan-iish iwe wenji giizhooziwe,
wenji ashamigowin, wenji bami'igomin. Mi'iwe daa ayaag
iwe mi-nonaagwad waabooyaan a'a bimaadizisin migo iwe,
miinage.mamawi' gotaamowawin gitaa aanikoobijigan mii'
ino gegoowan. Api nimaam-inonendam iwe inaakonigewin,
mii'iwen inowaan iko naagadaweniman.

Wiji aa'aag maajii azhegiwe'ad, wiji aa'aag maajii
nisidawendamowad minowaa! Gikendan na, gii
biminizha'amin bakaan miikanens, gaa gii biminizha'sii iwe
gwayako miikanens ozaam iwe gaa ashoodakamiginaad,
ozaam iwe zhooniyaa-izhijigewin, ozaam inowaan
izhijigewinan gegoowan. Igiwe oshki aa'aag maajii ikido,
"Gawiin." Giji gete aa'aag ekidowad, "Gawiin!"

Gakina gegoo gaa nandawenjigadag ayaam ima aki. Gakinda
gegoo gaa nandawenjigadag ayaam iwedi aanakwad. Iwe ayaa
biinji animikiikaa, iwe ayaa manidookewinan, Gaa anishaa
ni-kidose. Gakina gegoo nandawenjigadag imo ayaa, gwayak
doodatiwin, gaa izhi ogimaakandimang giinetawind-gakia geoo
ima ayaa.

Gitaa ayaamin aanike izhijigewinan. Gawiin gegoo
bitaakwiingwesid iwe, gakina gegoo i'i zagaabii'wan iwe.
Gishphin aa'aag onan-danmowad ji bakwaakbinidiziwad iwe
gaye wii baapinendamowad ino bigwajaya'ii inaakonigewinan,
mii api iwe aki jii nishwanaajigede

So, people can say all they want about my rants... But I will tell you something, at the end of the day it is going to be those laws, it is going to be that beautiful blanket of life that will keep us warm, that will keep us fed, that will nourish us. It will be that beautiful blanket of life that will, of course, provide our future generations with those things. When I think about law, that is what I think about.

Our people are starting to go back, our people are starting to recognize again! Do you know what, we followed the wrong path, we did not follow the right path because of colonization, because of capitalism, because of all those "ism" things. Our young people are starting to say, "No." Our Elders are saying, "No!"

Everything we need is on the land. Everything we need is in those clouds. It is in the thunder, it is in the ceremonies, I kid you not. Everything that we need is there, how to act right with each other, how to govern ourselves—everything is there.

We have our own traditional systems. There is nothing that is immune to that, everything is connected to that. If people decide to pull themselves out of it and not respect those natural laws, then the Earth will be destroyed.

Mii iwe gaa waabideman noongom. Igi niizho-okaadewad maajaa noojitoonwad jii ba-naajitoowad o'o aki, gaye gii daa ayaamin a'a aadizookaan, iwe aadizookaan, noongom. Ozaam aa'aag azhe-pikwanawad ino inaaki-nogewinan, naawaaj iwe wii izhawad An-ishinaabe inaakinogewin maawanji'idiwad gaye gikidon inaakonigewinensan , naawaaj iwedie wii izhaad giji-onashowewigamig mii' gikidon inaakonigewinensan gaye onashowewinan day-igoj gaa jii zaagitawage mii geget jii bizinda-mowa iwe aki izhi biinajimod.

Mii' ekido izhaa anishinaabewi gii waangoo-mimin ino inaakoginewanan, gii waangoomanan ige awesiinsag ji inawendiwin. Mii gaa aangoo-maad iwe aanakwad, gaa aangoomaad igiwe mitigoog gaye iwe dagwi mashkikiwan ani Azhi-gane-ayi'ii gaa oode, mii' jii nisidawmiing ino inaakoginewinan, gaa waniikesii awenen geget giinawind.

Mii iwedi babaa ezhaag gaye aangoomog, maajii inawendiwin iwedi noopimiing, maajii ozhi' inawemaaganag miziwe i'i aki.

That is what we are seeing now. The two-legged are on a quest to destroy the Earth, and we are in a sacred story, aadizookaan, right now. Because people turn their back on those laws, they would rather go to the Indian Act meetings and talk policy, they would rather go to the Parliament buildings and talk policy and legislation instead of sticking their ears out and really listening to what the land is telling us.

They say that as Anishinaabe people we adopt those laws, we adopt those animals to be our relatives. We adopt those clouds, we adopt those trees and those medicines to become a part of our families so that we understand those laws, so that we do not forget who we really are.

So go out there and adopt, start making relatives in the forest, start making relatives all over the lands.

Dibaajimowin owa Zhigaak

Iwe dibaajimowin mewinzha gii noondan a'a zhigaak.
Gii babaayaan iwe minis, gii windam-ago iwe minis gii
amanisookaade minis gaye gaanewiya jii izhaad iwedi minis.
Gii ga gwede. "Wegonesh iwedie onji aman-isookaadeg
minis?"

"Aaniish gegoowan onji' izhise iwedie mewinsha"

"Onh, wegonesh gaa izhiseg?' Ndikid.

Mii Iwa dibaajimowin:

I'i mindimooyenh gii inadizi iwed, gaa ma-maanjinowinini.
Daa ayaan giji mashkawni o manidooke. Daa ayaan gaa
mashkaw animikiikaa gaye waaseseg. Gii' nitaawigi gaye gaa
abid iwe minis. Nibyo aa'aag gii nibo, aa'aag apane gaa ikido
mii'iwa gaa izhijiged. Ozhiwinzo Nadamoyenh.

Gabaya'ii gii bimaadizi gete'ii igo. Aa'aag gawiin
minawenimasii ini. Igi apane gaa inamanji'wad gaa
apenimondawin gaa nishiwed aa'aag ima danakiiwin.
Gaa izhinizha'wag nibyo oshkinini-wag jii ninisaa ini. Gii
zagaswe'idiwag. Gaa izhi wiindamawad ige oshkininiwag
"Izhaag iwedi mii gii gaa nisaa iwe mindimooyenh. Baganaam
oshtigwaan. Gegoo zagizikan."

CHAPTER FOURTEEN

Story of the Skunk

This is a story I heard a long time ago about a skunk. I was going by an island, and they told me this island is a haunted island and nobody is to go to that island. I asked, "Why is that a haunted island?"

"Well things happened there a long time."

"Oh, what happened?" I said.

Here is the story:

An old lady lived there, and she was a sorcerer. She had very strong power. She had the power of thunder and lightning. She was born and lived on that island. A lot of people that died, people always said that she was the one that did it. Her name was Nadamoyenh.

She lived to be quite old. People did not like her. Nobody liked her. They always felt she was responsible for killing people in the village. They sent a bunch of young men to go kill her. They had a council meeting. They advised those young men "Go over there and kill that old lady. Club her head. Don't be scared."

Gaa odabwi iwedi jiimaan. Gii nisiwag gaa maajaawad. Niizho ikido "Giin iwedi ish-pi'izhaan, gii gaa baganaa'anan mii gaa nisaanan. Giin ima ayaan jiimaaning gishpin bi izhiga'sii gaa dibaajim gaa izhiseg.

Geget, gagwe-giimoozkawaan ini Nadamoyenh. Mii' jiiga'ii gii ayaad ini, gii ayaa ima wi-igwaasaatig iwedi. Mii' wiiweginigaazowad ino wadikwanan gaa mamaanjigopinaag. Igi gwi-inziensag gaa ji mamaajii'sii. Ino wadikwanan minjiminidaw gaa niizhowad ziinji'awag.

Ekido, "Gikendad giibi'izhayan wi'nishiwi. Onji gikendaman inowaan bagamaaganan biinji'oninjii. Maazhijigewin iwe gaa izhi bimaajiiweg." Gi namadabi niigaani ino mitig, gaa izhi maajii nagamod. Gezikaa, biidaa-nakwaya. Mii' eta nagamod onagomowin. Geg aapii, Ini aanakwad maajii obiiminashgagowan. Mii' gii ayabi nnaagamod onagomowin.. Mii' gezikaa, waawaatese niisina gaa baaginewaatig mii' gii nibo igi niizho-ozhininiwag.

Iwe oshkinini gaa ayaad ima jiimaan jiigibiig ogii waabidan iwe mii' wewiib odabwi gii'azhe. Gii dibaajimo igi aa'aag gaa izhise. Gaa ani giji ze-gizigiwaad iniwaan gii'aayaad iwe giji manidookewin. Giji manidookewin.

Mii gaa nikaa ogii ayaawasi' abinoojiiyenhwag. Endizha'wadizi igo obimaadiziwin gaye inini de-minik jii bimaadizid ini mindimooyenh ozaam omanidookewin zoongi'ani. Gii wiidigemad in-iniwan mii' azhe nibo. Mii' ezhi wiidigemad bakaan miinowa azhe nibo. Geg aapii, igi inini-wag ishkwaa gegweji'imaad ino. Mii' giji an-dawendang ji'ayaawad biibiyens.

They paddled there by canoe. There were three of them that left. Two of them said "you go up there, we'll club her and kill her. You stay in the canoe in case something happens. If we do not get back, you can go tell others what happened."

Of course, they tried to sneak up on Nadamoyenh. When they got closer to her, there was a birch tree there. It wrapped its branches around them and held them firm. The boys could not move. The branches were holding the two of them tight.

She said, "I know you've come to kill me. I can tell by the clubs in your hand. That wasn't a good move." She sat down in front of that tree, and she started to sing. Suddenly, clouds started to come. She just kept singing her song. Finally, those clouds started to twirl around them. She kept singing that song. All of a sudden, lightning came down and struck that tree and killed those two young men.

The young man in the canoe at the shoreline saw this and quickly paddled back. He told people what happened. They were very scared of her that she had great power. Great power.

But she never had any kids. Nadamoyenh was old. She lived her whole life and no man would live long enough with her as her power was too great. She would marry a man and he would die. She would marry another one, and he would die. So finally, the men stopped trying to marry her. But she really wanted to have a baby.

Mii', gaa izhizhaa ingoji zaaga'igan, gaye maaji gaa ganoonad
iwe giizhigoon. Ikido, "Gikendan, ima nidanakii'aan moozheg
igo. Azhaa daa gete aawii mii' eta aandandamaan ji'ayaawag
biibiyens." Gezikaa waawaatese biniisayaa gaa izhi baagiigaazo
migo ima oshtigwaan. Gaa wanendamaa ima jiimaan gaye
gaa maadaa'anoon azhegiiwe'inogazo iwedi minis. Mii' gii
goshkozi' iwedi. Gego api, aani biikojiise. misa wii'ayaawad
abinoojiiyens.

Iwe biibiyens ayaad getewaawendaagozi abinoojiiyens, mii'
apane ganoonad endaso-giizhik. Aa'aag onjii iwe danakiiwin
mii' baamishaa iwedi minis. Ogikendanaan gegoo izhiwebag.
Mashkiki aa'aag gikendanawan gegoo izhiseg, mii' gaa
gikdendasii wegonen.

Gi bami'an ino biibiyensan ini nagamonan. Mii'
nitaawiginaawaso ini biibiyensab]n gaye iwe abinoonijiyens
gaa zaagajii' biini'waabishkizi. Minonaagwad waabishkindibe,
waabishkazhe, wenge waabishkizi. Gaa apiitendagozi iwe
abinoonjiyens. Gakina gaa waabishkiziwad awesiinsag
apiitendagozi. Waabishki-mooz. Iwe waabishki gaagaagiw
ga babaamashe. Wenge apiji apiitendagozi. Misa, gibi
zaagajii' inake, Nadamoyenh ogikendan giiji manitookewi,
apiitendagozi biibiyens. Gii ombigi'aawaso ini abinoonjiyens
wiineta.

Obiibiyensan izhi wiinzo Ona'we.

Nadamoyenh ogii aanawenima' ininiwag; ozhiingenima':
" Gakina igiwe ininiwagm moozhag apane noojitoowad
bezhig gegoo apanii. Igiwe gagwe babaamenimigo. Mii' inake
omibigi'aad One'we inake'ii.

So, she went out on the lake, and she talked to the sky. She said "you know, I've lived here for all these years. I'm getting older now and I just want to have a baby." Suddenly lightning came down and struck her right in the head. She passed out in the canoe and the waves took her back to the island. She woke up there. Pretty soon, her stomach started to get bigger. She was going to have a baby.

That baby was a sacred baby. She always talked to that baby, every single day. People from the village would paddle around that island. They knew something was going on. Medicine people knew something was happening, but they did not know what.

She nurtured that baby through songs. She gave birth to that baby and that baby came out pure white. Beautiful white hair, white skin, just white. She was a special baby. All white animals are sacred. White moose. That white raven that flies around. They are very sacred. So, when she came out like that, Nadamoyenh knew this was a very powerful, special baby. She raised that baby alone.

Her baby's name was Ona'we.

Nadamoyenh didn't like men; she hated them: "All these men, they're always after one thing all the time. Do not trust them all the time. They're always trying to bother you." She raised Ona'we like that.

Geg aapi, izhi'ayaawan makoonsiwi. Mii' aapi, Ona'we ayad gaa minonaagwad, waabishkawaa, gagaanwaanikwe, apikaazo. Oshkiinzhigoon iwe onizhishinoon gaye oginiiwaande. Ozhaga'e gii zhooshkwazhe. Gaa izhiw apiitendagozi, apiji apiitendagozi. Gaa izhi maajaa mii' nan-dawaabamad wii' onaabemi iwedi danakiiwin.

Nibyo ininiwag bi naaskowaa naazikawgo' gaa nooji'ikwewe ini. Appijii wiiba dagozhiing da-goshin iwe agamiing, gakina oshki-ininiwag mii dezhi ayaawad iwedi obabigwanan, bibigwenaad. Ezhi namadabi niigaanii o'o bezhig ini-ni bibigwenaad iwe babigwan mii'onishkaa gaye namadabi niigaani bakaan miinowa, mii' bakaan miinowa. Daa oganawaabgamaa gakina igiwe.

Ogikendanawa gi apiitendagozi gi ayaad apiitendagoziwin mamaandaawizinan. Mii' iwe onji misawendamowa wiiji'aad ini. Geg aapi, oganawaabgamaa igiwe gakina ininiwag kido "Ganmawiin noongom. Maagizhaa bakaan minawaa."

Mii' ayaa a'a mashkikinini ima danakiiwin. Mii' inendan "Mii'waa ni'niiwiiw. Niin gaa nooji'iwe." Noowaaj igo gii zaziikizi gaye giji zoongi'iwi. Goding, gii azhagewe iwe danakiiwin, obizindamowaa ini bibigwenaad ini bib-igwanan gaye wiindamawa' igiwe, "Gawiin ga-nabaj, gawiin aapi." Mii'igo iwe gaa izhiseg iwe gagaanwenzh.

Geg aapi, Iwe mashkikinini obiwaabiman mii ikido, "Gikenda gawiin bibigwesiimoon nbibig-wan." Mii' ikido "Daga'sa, gItojige-boodaajigen. Ninadawen bizidan gi'nagamowin." Gaa izhi namadabi maajii bibigwe obibigwan. Ikwe ikido, "Iwe apiji minotaagwad mii' nii baabii'o."

Finally, it was time of age. By then, Ona'we had beautiful, white, long hair, braided. Her eyes were nice and pink. Her skin was just flawless. She was sacred, very sacred. She went off to find a husband in the village.

A lot of men would come up to her and try to court her. As soon as she came up to the shoreline, all the young men would be there with their flutes, playing. She would sit there in front of one man playing the flute and she would get up and sit in front of another one, then another one. She would look at all of them.

They knew she was sacred and had special powers. That is why they wanted to be with her. Finally, she looked at all those men and said "Maybe not today. Maybe another time."

But there was a medicine man in the village. He thought, "She's going to be my wife. I'll get her." He was older and very powerful. Occasionally, she would go back to the village, she would listen to them playing their flutes and she would say to them, "I don't think so, not now." That went on for a quite a while.

Finally, that medicine man came up to her and said, "You know I never played my flute for you." She said, "Well, play it. I want to hear your song." He sat down and played his flute. She said, "That's very beautiful but I'm going to wait."

Gaa izhi ishkendam. Gawiin wi'odaapinigesii iwe
aanawenimind ini. Gaa azhekwanshiwiid iwedi minis. Mii' ani
azhaa igi aa'aag misa ba-baadizhimad ini, ekido "Mii' gegoo
inaapine iwe. Aawi maji-manidoo. Ozhiingenima' inini-wag,
migo naasaab dibishkoo omaamaayan. Ji'eta gegoo izhijigetaw.
Ji'eta ji doodawin iwe."

Gete aa'aag gii ikido, "Gawiin gegoo inaapinesii iwe. Mii'eta
mino-izhewebizi. Na'idaa be izhad ima, mii'eta waabinagog
mino-izhewebiziwin. Ganawendizo; debaanagwad gaa
izhinaagozi. Ayaa apiitendagoziwi' gego migoshkaaji'ikan."

Idash gaa gikaawinaa igiwe niizho oshkininnwad gaa nisa' o'o
mindimooyenh, Nadamoyenh, ikido, "Gaa wiiji'igo." Mii'gaa
izhijige iko azhaawad noopimiing daso giizhig, gaye gii bi
zaaga'iwaad ogii ayaawan nibyo biiza'ojiibikaang.

Mii'iwa ikidowad, "Gagaweiji'gidan ini ojiibik mii' gashkitaw
jii webinid. Gemaa gaye gii' zoongi'iwi maagizhaa iwe ogii
nisigoon. Ni-misawendamin gwaya izhiwebiziwinan gaa igi'
izhised igiwe ninoozisag. Misa, nii'odaapinanan odaanisan."
Mii' iwedi mashkikinini inendam, aahaaw nigagaweji'gidan ino
ojiibik.

Ona'we azhegwe iwedi danakiiwin ayaapii gaye bizindaw a'a
bibigwan bibigwe. Mii' iwedi mashkikinini daa izhi bibigwe
obibigwan. Ogi ayaan mino giji'akik i'i naaboob ima niigaanii
okadan megwaa namadabi bibigwe iwe bibig-wan.

Mii'wiindamaw ini, "Gikendan, ni-giganawaabamin. Gawiin
odaapanesii iwe inini. Indapiitendan iwe. Mii', nimisawendan
gimiinin iwe miijimens gaa wii bagijigan. Inapitenindiz-iwin,
Gitan iwe miijim." Ezhi'inendan, "Gii'minonaadiz inini." Ezhi
wayezhima ine. Maajii gitaad iwe nabob. Gezikaa aazhigijishin.
Iwe migo ima zhingishing; basangwaabi,

He got upset. He could not take being rejected by her. She paddled back to the island. He started to go to the people and gossip about her, saying, "There's something wrong with her. She is evil. She does not like men, she is just like her mom. We must do something. We have to get rid of her."

The old people said, "No there is nothing wrong with her. She has been polite. Every time she has come here, she has shown good manners. She takes care of herself; you can tell by the way she looks. She is sacred so don't bother her."

But the grandparents of those two young men that were murdered by that old lady, Nadamoyenh, said, "We'll help you." What they did was they went into the forest for many days, and they came out with a bunch of pounded roots.

They said, "Get her to eat these roots and you'll get rid of her. Maybe she is powerful but maybe this will kill her. We want justice for what happened to our grandchildren. So, we're going to take her daughter." So that medicine man thought, okay I will get her to eat these roots.

Ona'we would go back to the village every once in a while, and listen to the flute playing. There the medicine man was playing his flute. He had a nice big pot of soup in front of his legs as he sat there playing the flute.

He told her, "You know, I've been watching you. You do not take a man. I respect that. So, I want to give this food to you as an offering. You respect yourself. Eat this food." She thought, "You're a nice man." He deceived her. She started to eat that soup. Suddenly, she fell backwards. She laid there; her eyes closed.

Gakina ininiwag gii ikido, "Gawiin ogii an-dawenimigonan gakina giinawind. Gagwe-gojitoomin idash giji inenimo ozaam inandam noonwaj wiin babenak gakina awii'aa apiij ozaam gii waabishkindibe." Mii'iwe gaa ikido. "Mii'ima ganaganana mii' owiiyaw dezhi ba-naadad iwedi." Ayaawag gotaamigwendaagwad.

Gii ani gigizheb, gii azhangiwe debaabamaad inowaan owiiyaw, mii' ima izhishiing iwe opikwanang iwe zhigaag. A'a onizhishi zhigaa-gens. Gawwin ogii nisaasii. Mii' eta gaa'izhised'aa ino zhigaag. Mii'gii nishkaadizi. Babaa izhaa ima danakiiwin gaye maajii boojigidawa' igiwe ininiwag mii' gaa ozhiingen-imaad.

Gakina igiwe gegwa'nisaa inowaan. Noonwaj gii gizhiikaw gaye zoongi-adizi. Mii' bana'awad jii nisaa. Booshka iwe mashkikinini banaa'ad jii nisaa. Mii' izhi aakozid gaa izhimaagwad. Mijii zhishigagowed gaye aa'aagadeshka. Wenge nishkaadizi, mii'eta boojigidawa' gakina igiwedi.

Gibezhigwan apii, awesiinsag gaa ayaawad noopimiing maajii ginawaabiya ino gaye. Maajii nagamowad onagamowinan. Misa izhaa biinji noopimiing mii' gakina igiwe awesiinsag ekido gii daa aawi niwiiw. Mii' izhi ikido "Gawiin, ge-maa gaa bi azhegiwe." Mii' gaa izhijiged aayapii.

Iwe okomis, Nadamoyenh, wenge nishkaadizi. Megwaa iwe izhiseg,, mii inendamowin aaniin gaa izhi nisigwa igiwe gakina aa'aag. Mii'dash geget, Ona'we ezhijiged igo oshki'aa gaa izhi-jige, babaawaabijige, babaa debaabamadang gegoo daa gagiibaadizi, babaa boogijina' aa'aag

Geg apii, igi awesiinsag maajii omiigaanigo' gaye. "Gawiin onendandasii wiijii'igosinaan, Gii daa nisaanan." Mii'iwa gaa ikidowad. Mii' eta gakina miigaanawad ini.

All the men said, "She didn't want us. She rejected all of us. We tried but she's too stuck up because she thinks she's better than everybody because she has white hair." That is what they said. "Let's leave her there and let her body just rot there." They were being horrible.

The next morning, they went to go check up on her body, and there laying on its back was a skunk. A beautiful little skunk. It did not kill her. It just turned her into a skunk. And she was mad. She went around the village and started spraying all those men and they hated her.

They all tried to kill her. She was too fast and too strong. They could not kill her. Even that medicine man could not kill her. They would get sick by that smell. They would throw up and gag. She was so mad, she just sprayed all of them.

At the same time, the animals in the forest started to have eyes for her too. They started to sing their songs. So, she would go into the forest and all those animals would say you should be my wife. She would say, "No, maybe I'll come back." She did that for quite a while.

The grandmother, Nadamoyenh, was livid. While this was going on, she kept thinking of how she could kill all those people. But of course, Ona'we was doing her thing as a young person, looking around, checking things out, being mischievous, spraying people.

Finally, the animals started to turn on her too. "She doesn't want to be with any of us. We should kill her." That's what they said. They just all turned on her.

Gii minonaadizi, apane minonaadiziwi gakina aawii'aa, gakina awesiinsag, igi mitigoog, igi gitigaadanan, igi aanakwadan, igi anagoog, gaki-na gegoo. Gii mino-izhewebizi.

Gaa izhi wiizhaawimaan ji bagizo'. Mii'enendamowaa, "Ima biingji ayaad, daa ayaawag aa'aag, gaa'ayawanaan mikinaak, gaye gaa ayaawanaan igiwe ininabikoog mii'gaye inowaan biiminaakwaanan dakobijigazo'og mii'dash gaa dakobinaanan ima okaading, mii gaa izhi gozabii." Mikinaak iwe gi debwetam jii izhiged. Gakina dezhi bagizo' iwedi mii' mik-inaak moozhkamo giji ininabikon ayaawan mii' ashi akobinaad ima inowaan okaading megwaa dezhi bagizonid, mii' gonzaabiid ima mitaamik. Gegaa igo nisaabaawe.

Ookomisan gi nishkaadizi. Wegne nishkaadizi. Gizeka, ima ga'aayaad, gizhibaajiwan maajiiseg. Gakina igiwe awesiinsag ima gaa ayaad gii wiikwamada gaye izhi nisaabaawe ima gizhi-baajiwaning. Migo ima gaa gi'aayaad wenge baatewakamigaa. Iwe gizhibaajiwan migo oditibishkagon. Geget, obimaaji'aan. Ookomis-an gibimaaji'goon, giishkizhang ini ininabikon ima okaading, mii ogiiwewinan, izhigewe iwedi minis.

Ikido, "Gaa gagwannisagakamigan aki ingoji. Nibyo igiwe ininiwag gaa gego jii gikendamow-ad. Igi wanishinog gaa bimi'ayaad. Mii' gaa ikid-owan, igi apane noojitoowad gegoo bezhig mozhag igo. Mi'igo apane ji'odaapinaamowad wengonan igo andewendamowad. Mii' izhigo jii maajaa'an. Daa ninendam gaye nibagosendam gabaya'ii gaye enigok iwe gaa wii izhijigeyan gaye aaniish inaa gaa izhi bimi'aadiziwin.

"Mii', wii'izhigeyan, niiwo-giizhigag, nI igo-shimo'. Ishkwaasak i'i ingoshimowan, gii nan-dawendan jibi-izhaa'an ni' wiigiwaam gaye nan-dawenamin ji gitaman niwiiyaw. Jii aabin-dami'in mii' gagaminogowiz gakina ni mamaan-daawizin. Mii'inake gaa izhi naadamaazowin mii' maajaa'an."

She was nice, always nice to everybody, to all the animals, the trees, the plants, the clouds, the stars, everything. She was polite.

They invited her to go swimming. They thought, "When she is in there, we will have people, we will have turtle, and we will have these rocks with these ropes tied and we will tie them to her legs, and she will just sink down." Turtle was the one that agreed to do that. They were all swimming there and turtle came up with a big rock and tied it to her leg when she was swimming, and she sank right down to the bottom. She almost drowned.

Grandma was mad. Very mad. Suddenly, right where she was, a whirlpool started to happen. All those animals that were there got sucked in and drowned in that whirlpool. Right where she was it was dry ground. That whirlpool was right around her. Of course, she was saved. Her grandmother saved her, cut that rock from her leg, and took her home, back to the island.

She said, "It's an awful world out there. A lot of those men do not know anything. They have lost their way. Like I said, they are always after one thing all the time. They always try to take whatever they want. It is getting close to my time to go. I have thought and I have prayed long and hard about what I am going to do and how you are going to live your life.

"So, what I am going to do is, in four days' time, I am going to fast. After my fast is over, I want you to come into my lodge and I want you to eat my body. Devour me and it will give all my power to you. That way you'll be able to defend yourself after I'm gone."

Gaa o'igoshimo gii niiwo-giizhig. Iwe shigaa-goons,
Ona'we, biindiged iwe igoshimowi-nagamik gaa gaye maajii
zhaashaagijiged o'o okaad. Zhemaak maajii wiisini iwe,
odookishkan giyaabii mamaandaawiz biinji ayaani, gaa ani-
mindido. Geg aapii, gakina ogitan i'i okaad. Iwe zhigaag gegaa
ani mindido' a'a animoosh. Mii' gitan iwe bakaan okaad, gaye
iwe zhigaag ani mangigi zhigo niiomizid. Gaa maajii gitaad oni-
kaan mii zhigo iwe zhigaag mii' ani ayaad ingodwaasomizid.
Mii giyaabi gitaamowad okomisan, mii' giyaabi zhigaag ani
mangigi. Geg aapii, iwe zhigaag giji mindido'. Gaa mizhi-wiid.
Biinish, maajii gitaan iwe okomisan wiinindiban mii' ima gaa
odinan awashime mamaan-daawiziwin. Mii'iwe gaa zhi giji
mindido.

Gii nIshkaadizi, Mii' onji nishkaadizi ozaam okomisan gii nibo.
Onishkaanima gakina inini-wag gaa gigwe migoshkaaji'gwad.
Onishkaanima' gakina ininiwag ini okomisan. Ozaam igi ayaan
okomisan omamaandaawiziwin biinji' ogii ayaan, gaye iwe
nishkenindiwin giyaabii ogi ayaan, maajii mawine'an igi aa'aag.

Gaa izhimaagozi wenge niboowi'maagwad, migo nisigowad.
Mii' eta miji nisaad ininiwag apane. Gaa miji boogijina igiwedi,
gaye mii' ezhi miji bangishinowad gaye izhi akoziwad mii'
izhi maajii gitaamowa'. Babaa azhaa inowaan dana-kiiwin
miinowaa bakaan danakiiwin gaa miji nisaad ininiwag ezhi
gitaamowad. Wegne giji zoongi'iwi.

Igi aa'aag ani giji zegiziwad. Mii' moozhag geg-we gibiji'aad
ini, mii' bwaanawitoon, Aa'aag gawiin ji odaminowad
agwajiing, mii eta en-daad ayaad. Gaa izhimaagowang
nibowi'magwad. Gaa izhimaagwag zoongi'ayaa. Mi'igo ji nizi-
gowin miji bijimaandiman. Gaa miji boogidid miziwe inowaan
danakiiwinan apane igo geget aa'aag miji bangishin nibo'.

She fasted for four days. That little skunk, Ona'we, went into that fasting lodge and started nibbling on her leg. As soon as she started eating it, she felt more power inside of her, and she started to get bigger. Finally, she ate all her leg. That skunk was about as big as a dog. Then she ate her other leg, and that skunk grew about four feet. She started to eat the arms and pretty soon that skunk was six feet tall. The more she ate of her grandmother, the more that skunk grew. Pretty soon, that skunk was big. It was a giant. So finally, she started to eat her grandmother's brains and that is when she got the most power. That is how she got so big.

She was mad. She was mad that her grandmother died. She was mad at all the men that tried to bother her. She was mad at all the men that tried to bother her grandmother. Because she had her grandmother's power inside of her, and that resentment was inside of her, she started to attack the humans.

Her smell was so deadly, it would kill them. She just killed men most of the time. She would spray them, and they would fall and get sick and then she would eat them. She would just go from village to village and just kill men and eat them. She was a very powerful being.

The people got really scared. They kept trying to stop her, but they could not. People were not playing outside; they were staying home. That smell was deadly. That smell was powerful. It could kill you even if you smelled it. She would spray all around the villages all the time and people would just drop dead.

Geg aapii, iwe oshki ikwezens, okomisan odibaajimo ini "Gikendan wenje doodang: igi ininiwag ezhi'aad inake. Ayaa eta bezhig aa'aa gaa wiidookaazo. A'a Nenaboozhoo. Jeta jii gagwe ayaawa'ing Nenabozhoo. Nenaboozhoo gawiin daa bizindawgosii, shke Nenaboozhoo giin gaa bizindaa. Nenaboozhoo daa ayaa iwe ininabikoog. Bibaagin owizowin niiwing mii' gaa bi naazikaw gaa izhi bii'.

Gaa izhi bibaagi o'o owizowin niiwing gaa bii'o daso-giizhig. Gezika Nenaboozhoo bibimose gaye wiijii'aad wiijiiwaaganan wiji'igoon, Pakwus. Apane miigaadiwag mii'ayaawad goding mino-giizhigad.

Ikwezens ikido, "Iwe mangigi zhigaag, Ona'we onisaa' gakina awii'aa gaye mii' gaq gikendazii geizhijigeng. Gi inendamingo ji nisaad iwedi zhigaag." Nenaboozhoo gaganoonaand Pakwas. "Wengonen gaa izhijigeying?"

Ezhi ikido, "Gikendan gaa izhijigeyan. Iwe ikido "Ona'we daa ayaan mamaandaawiziwin i'i waawaasese; waabidan ino waabishkaw beshaag. Gaa ozhidoonmin zhimaagan iwe baa-ginewaatig ozhidoon, Bowaagtig, mii'ima gaa bashiba'wi ima ezhi bagoneyaa gaa boogidid onji zaagashkaa. Gaa biinisidoon wasa igo baa-maa ode dookinind. Ogaa nisigoon.

Pakwas gaye Nenaboozhoo gidaabaajimo iwe gibayii igo. Nenaboozhoo ikido "Gawiin, gaa izhigesii iwe. Indawaaj bashiba'wi ino ode', gaa nanaandawi' ini ode'. Gaa naazikawanan iwe Bowaagtig, iwe baaginewaatig mii' dakobidoon mashkiki ima ishkwe-ayi'ii, gaa biinisidoon ima gaa boogidid, mii'igo gakina biinji'ii iwedie gaa atoon iwe mashkik biinji ode'. Mii' naa'ii iwe, gawiin igo gagiibaaji'ayaa. Misa daa gwaykose gegoon.

Finally, there was a young girl, and her grandmother was telling her "You know why she's doing that: the men turned her into that. There is only one person that could help us. It is Nenaboozhoo. We must try to get Nenaboozhoo. Nenaboozhoo is not going to listen to me, but Nenaboozhoo will listen to you. Nenaboozhoo will be in the rocks. Call his name four times and he'll come to you and wait."

She called his name four times and she waited for many days. Suddenly Nenaboozhoo came walking along and he had his friend with him, Pakwus. They were always fighting but they had their good days.

The girl said, "This giant skunk, Ona'we, is killing everybody and we don't know what to do. We want you to kill that skunk." Nenaboozhoo talked to Pakwus. "What should we do?"

He said, "I know what to do. He said, "Ona'we has the power of lightning; look at those white stripes. We will make a spear out of a tree that was struck by lightning, Bowaagtig, and we will spear her right in that hole where that spray comes out. We will shove it in there as far as we can until it reaches her heart. It'll kill her."

Pakwus and Nenaboozhoo talked about it for a while. Nenaboozhoo said "No, we're not going to do that. Instead of stabbing her heart, we are going to help heal her heart. We will get that Bowaagtig, that stick hit by lightning, but we are going to tie a medicine at the end, and we are going to shove that where she sprays from, and we are going to shove it all the way in there and put the medicine into her heart. That will fix her, so she is not so bad. And we'll restore everything back."

Geget mii' iwe gaa izhijigewad. Gii naazikwaad baaginewaatig, mii' gaa atoowad mashkiki ish-kwe-ayi'ii gaa izhi gaashiboodoonwad. Gaa izhi andaweni'aad ini daso-giizhig. Geg aapii, mikwaa, mii' gi debitoowaa iwe mitigoons gaanjiwebinamowad ini. Iwe mashkiki mash-kimodens ibideg ode', mii' ima gaa gijiseg, gaa izhi ikobidoon iwe mitigoons. Gaa izhi maajii odaapishkaa, gaa iniginowad api.

Nenaboozhoo owiindaman, "Gigikendamin wenji doodaman iwe gaa doodaman. Gii wiijii bebwetago. Jii eta bakaan gegoo jimikamiing. Iwe gii boogidewin gaa ayaan apiji zoongi'ayaa. Indawaaj nisaasii ininiwag, gii waabijitoonmi iwe boogidewin a'a mashkiki jii wiidookwawi aa'aag. Boogijizh waaboo iwe gaa izhi-wiindemin.

Inake gaa izhi naganaad ini. Gii miigwechiwin-dam ozaam ogikenda gaababaamandan gii maa-naajiged, gaye daa gwayakwaa miinowaa. Mii'iwe Boogijizh waaboo, iwe mashkiki, ji waabita daa wiidookwawi igi aa'aag.

Gi ayabii ima ayaa gaye awashime zoongi'aya. Inendam, "Mi'igo ozaam ishkwaaj nizhijigewin ji inenimag nii'okomis, ni waabijitoon iwe bangi ayaawan mamaandaawiziwin ji izhise'ad igi maja ininiwag ji'izhise zhigaagagwag gaye nawa dibishko niin."

Gaa izhijigad. Dibikag izhaa iwedi owiigiwaami-yan, mii' gaa boogiji' igiwe, misa goshkozi' gii zhigaagiwi. Aa'aad ogikendanaa iwe, mii'dash gaa izhi'ikidowad, "Amanj igo gishpin ni'inawemaagan gemaa gaya gawiin, mii gawiin ji amoond igiwedi."

Nibyo aaaag daa amowasii zhigaag; gaa bagidi-naasiiwag ozaam wegonen odinamaagen. Mii' iwe zhigaag gaa bi ayaad gaa izhi gekenimawiing noongom.

So that is what they did. They got a stick that was hit by lightning, and they put medicine at the end of it and they sharpened it. They hunted for her for many days. Finally, they found her, and they grabbed that stick and shoved it right in her. That medicine pouch went right to her heart, and it stayed there, and they pulled that stick out. She started to shrink, to the size they are now.

Nenaboozhoo told her, "We know why you did what you did. We agree with you. We must find another way. That spray you have is very powerful. Instead of killing men, we are going to use that spray as medicine to help people. Boogijizh waaboo is what that will be called."

They left her like that. She was thankful because she knew in her mind what she did was wrong, and things could be made right again. And that Boogijizh waaboo, that medicine, was going to be used to help the people.

She was there and still powerful. She thought, "Just because my last act to honour my grandmother, I'm going to use the last bit of my power to turn some of those evil men into skunks too so they can be like me."

She did. She went at nighttime into their lodges, and she sprayed them, and they woke up as skunks. People knew that, and after that said, "We don't know if that's our relative or not, so we can't eat them."

A lot of people do not eat skunk; they are not allowed because it could be their relative. That is how the skunk came to be as we know it today.

Iwe mashkiki wiinge giji zoongi'aya. Boogijizh waaboo i'i nandawe' aa'aag. Ozaam Ona'we gii nitaa miigaazo, nibyo ogi nisa', ogikendanawa iwe mashkiki gi mashkawi'aa inake. Mii' iwe nitaa miigaadan iwe aakosiwin mii'inake gaa izhi bibaadizi. Aa'aag apane noojitoonawa iwe mashkiki moozhag ozaam giji minose.

That medicine is very powerful. Boogijizh waaboo can cure people. Because Ona'we was such a fighter, she killed so many people, they know that the medicine is strong like that. It can fight off sickness the way she lived her life. People are always after that medicine all the time because it works so well.

Misi-Ginebekoog
gaye Aanid Manidoo-aya'aad

DAZHINDAMAW IWE OZHIBII'IGEWININI

Bomgiizhik (revolving Sky) Nimkii Aazhibikoong njibaa.
Giigoonhan doodeman. Ojibwe aawi. Niiwin gwenaajiwinjin
wdaansan wda'aawaan. Nongo megwaa daa mtigwaakiing. Nimkii
Aazhibikoong, Nishinaabekiing enaagdoot Nishinaabemowin
miinwaa mzinbiigeng, ngoj-go-gegoo baa nankiing maakiing. Aapji
gii-mnaabewzi, Bomgiizhik gii-bi-kogid, ghkendangwaa zhi-nishnaabe
maadzid, gi-giiwse, gii-zgaktaaso, gegookiing edinang.Aashi gaa-
bi-kenoomaagzid getsinjin gii-bi-ghkendmaad niibna nso-boon,
miinongo maanda enakiid, aadsookewnini aawi. Niibnaa go kinda
dbaajmowininan gashtoonanwii-mzinbii'ang ezhiwaambdvng,
miidash gonda mzinbiiganag kina mziwi king ewaambjigaazjig.
Bomgiizhik ge'e ngomwinan ezhtoojindo-ngamnan, miinwaa doo-
zhibii'aanan. Aapji go bishgendaan maandqa nankid, pii gwa zhised.
Naangodnong syaakyoojin waawaaskoneyan maage datganaabit
oodi gnawaambdang gwenaajwinik, gwenaajwang dibik giizhik.

Aapiji gwa naa nonggwa kina gegoo chi zhiwebat. Gaayii gwa wiikaa
e`bemaadizit gii bi waabdaziin nonngwaa ezhiwebiziiying. Weyiip
nonggwa gegoo bi aansemigat naasaap ge ezhiiyaamigak gojiing,
eshkam ge bi wiizho`oomgat. Ndoo ndwetaan wiigwa, lishpin kina
mi maamiwiizing maanda ji da akiiminaa, ka shkitamaami gwa. Pii
gaazimaaying Anishinaabek miinwaa ge ezhi maandaawshkewziwaad
miinwaa ezhi zoongde`eyaad, aapji gwa ka zoongaabwiimi. Ka
kinaagemi dash.

Serpents
and Other Spiritual Beings

ABOUT THE AUTHOR

Photo credit: Alex Usquiano

Bomgiizhik (Isaac Murdoch) is from Nimkii Aazhibikoong First Nation. He is of the Fish Clan and is Ojibwe. He has four beautiful children. He currently lives in the forest at Nimkii Aazhibikoong, an Indigenous community that focuses on Indigenous language, art, and land based activities. Being blessed with the opportunity, Bomgiizhik grew up in the traditional setting of hunting and gathering on the land. Having spent many years learning from Elders, he spends a lot of his time as a Story Teller. Many of these stories become his visual art pieces which have become recognized world wide. Bomgiizhik is also a Singer Song Writer who loves to make music when ever he gets a chance. You will often find him on the land looking at his favourite plants or gazing into the beautiful night sky.

We are in special times. Never in the History of Humanity have we been faced with the challenges that we are now. Climate change is here and the World is changing fast. I truly believe that when we put our hearts together and unite for the Earth and people, we can achieve anything. When we lift up our people and recognize the strengths and gifts of others, we can be a force of nature. Together we will win!

DASHINDAMAW IWE
ANNIKANOOTAAGEWIKWE

Pakwangwetook ndigo, Makwa ndoodem, Naotkamegwanning donji' bazigwii. Omaamaayan, niijikweyan, ozigoa'eyan, ookomisan gaye Nishiwewin Gikinoo'amaadiwigamig nizhaabwii (IRS) gaye nizhaabwii Anishinaabe Giizhig Gikinoo'amaadiwigamig. Giji-ashodamaagewin niiswi izhi debendaagozi. Gibi nitaawigi gigito iwe gete anishinaabemowin, gaye gii ganawenjige ino manidokenan gaye aki gikendaasowin boozhke iwe IRS wanishkwe'. Iwe nitam izhigiizhwewin i'i anishinabemowin; gikinoo'amowa jii gikinaamaaged iwe izhigiishwewin. Gii aanakanoojige igiwe NAN Inaakonigwewin Wiidookoodaadiwin, gii aanokii bizindamoo-makaoons gaa daapzhkoo aakoziikaazo aakoziiwigamigoon, aanakanoojige gaa maazinaatesi gagaanzonge iwe manidoobaa izhigiizhwewin. Pakwangwtook odiyan wemijigoozhi gikinoo'amaagewin noowaj omino dakonan giji Anishinaabe gikendaasowin oma ode' gawiin inowaan gikendaasowinan ishpi-gikendaasowinan, ozaam mii iwa gii Anishinaabewi. Ikido gii izhijiged wa izhijiged ezhi bimaadizi mii' noonde amajiwebinang iwe gete Anishinaabe bimaadiziwinan. Gii anokii bakaan iwedi miziwekamig paamaa boone-anokii iwe giji-mookimaan aki/Kanata agokiwaajiganeyaabiinoong, gaye Anishinaabe Inaakonegwin gii ogimaakaaniwi gaa oodenaawin mii' gaye apane wii zhooshkonamawge gete ogikendaasowinan.

ABOUT THE TRANSLATOR

Patricia BigGeorge grew up in Naotkamegwanning First Nation. Pakwangwetook ndigo, Makwa indoodem. She is a mother, sister, aunty, grandma, also a Genocide School Survivor (IRS) and survivor of Indian Day school. She is a Treaty #3 member. She grew up speaking her traditional language, and preserving ceremonies and land knowledge in spite of the IRS disruption. Her first language is Anishinaabemowin; she went to school to teach the language. She has done some translation for NAN Legal Services, worked with a radio skit for a hospital situation, translated cartoon skits with her dialect and a Manitoba dialect. Patricia has a western education but holds her traditional knowledge closer to her heart than another educational standard, because that is who she is as Anishinaabe. She says that she has done pretty much what she wanted to do in life but needs to awaken knowledge of the Anishinaabe traditional ways of life. She worked in westernized society until she retired from Customs, was an Indian Act elected chief for her community and is always willing to pass on the traditional knowledge that she has.